MANUAL ON
OIL POLLUTION
SECTION I - PREVENTION
2011 EDITION

INTERNATIONAL
MARITIME
ORGANIZATION

London, 2011

First published in 1983
by the INTERNATIONAL MARITIME ORGANIZATION
4 Albert Embankment, London SE1 7SR
www.imo.org

Second edition 2011

Printed in the United Kingdom by CPI Group (UK) Ltd, Croydon, CR0 4YY

ISBN: 978-92-801-4244-0

IMO PUBLICATION
Sales number: IA557E

H41064

Contents

Foreword

This publication was prepared by the OPRC-HNS Technical Group, a subsidiary body of IMO's Marine Environment Protection Committee. It replaces the 1983 edition of the *Manual on Oil Pollution, Section I – Prevention*. This revised edition significantly updates the information included in the previous edition and includes several new sections covering, in particular, prevention aspects of ship-to-ship transfers at sea and the prevention of pollution from ships in ice covered waters.

The *Manual on Oil Pollution, Section I* aims to provide useful information to assist governments, in particular those of developing countries, in taking appropriate measure to prevent or minimize operational and accidental pollution from ships, in accordance with the requirements of the International Convention for the Prevention of Pollution from Ships, 1973, as modified by the Protocol of 1978 relating thereto (MARPOL).

MARPOL is the main international convention aimed at protecting the marine environment from operational and accidental pollution from ships. Its six annexes regulate the prevention of marine pollution by oil, noxious liquid substances in bulk, harmful substances carried by sea in packaged form, sewage, and garbage, as well as the prevention of air pollution.

The *Manual on Oil Pollution* series consists of six sections:

Section I   Prevention (contained in this publication)

Section II   Contingency Planning (revised edition published 1995)

Section III   Salvage (revised edition published 1997)

Section IV   Combating Oil Spills (revised edition published 2005)

Section V   Administrative Aspects of Oil Pollution Response (revised edition published 2009)

Section VI   IMO Guidelines for Sampling and Identification of Oil Spills (published 1998)

A greater understanding of spill effects and damages has strengthened the resolve of many governments to focus efforts on prevention. The premise of this manual is that every oil spill, regardless of its size or its source, is worthy of prevention efforts at some level. It is widely understood that the size of an oil spill alone does not determine the degree of its resulting damage – either environmentally or economically.

This section of the *Manual on Oil Pollution* is intended to provide practical guidance, describing procedures for the handling of oil cargoes, bunkering, ship-to-ship transfer operations, transfer operations involving offshore units and operations in ice covered waters. It also provides an overview of the various practices, as a complement to the more detailed industry standards and codes of practice currently in place. The information provided does not supersede or replace any information, laws, or regulations contained in any other publications with respect to the waters and areas to which it pertains.

Glossary of abbreviations and definitions

berth	Piers, jetties, mooring buoys or similar installations to which the facilities are affixed, serving for the mooring of ships and for the conduct of oil transfer and ancillary operations.
CALM	Catenary anchor leg mooring system
CBM	Conventional buoy mooring system
COLREG	Convention on the International Regulations for Preventing Collisions at Sea, 1972.
COW	Crude oil washing of crude oil tanks.
differentiated compliance anchoring system (DICAS)	A positioning system using anchoring of the ship, allowing it to move in order better to accommodate variations in the environment to avoid fully parallel (in which the ship is fully head on to the weather) or fully crosswise (athwart to the weather) situations, based on the distribution and setting-up of mooring lines, which define differentiated degrees of rigidity (compliance) in the anchoring system.
dynamic positioning (DP)	A computer controlled system to automatically maintain a vessel's position and heading by using its own propellers and thrusters.
facility	Complex of equipment and systems, permanently mounted on or integral to the berth and designed for the transfer of oil, loading or unloading tanker, reception of dirty ballast and oil residues and for bunkering.

FPSO	A floating production, storage and offloading/offtake (FPSO) unit is a floating vessel used by the offshore industry for the processing of hydrocarbons and for storage of oil.
FSU	A floating vessel used only to store oil is referred to as a floating storage unit.
HELCOM	Helsinki Commission (Baltic Marine Environment Protection Commission)
hose	A flexible pipe with arrangements for connection to facility and ship.
IACS	International Association of Classification Societies
IAPH	International Association of Ports and Harbours
ice covered	Waters where local ice conditions present a structural risk to a ship.
ice navigator	Any individual who, in addition to being qualified under the STCW Convention, is specially trained and otherwise qualified to direct the movement of a ship in ice covered waters. Qualifications of an ice navigator should include documentary evidence of having completed on-the-job training, as appropriate, and may include simulation training.
ICS	International Chamber of Shipping
IGS	Inert gas system
ISGOTT	International safety guide for oil tankers and terminals
INTERTANKO	International Association of Independent Tanker Owners
ISM Code	International Safety Management Code
lightering	See "ship-to-ship transfer".
loading arm	Part of the facility consisting of hinged pipes and arrangements for their connection to tanker manifolds. The design of the loading arm may incorporate a permanently connected hose.
LOADLINE	International Convention on Load Lines, 1966
MARPOL	International Convention for the Prevention of Pollution from Ships, 1973, as modified by the Protocol of 1978 relating thereto
MEPC	IMO's Marine Environment Protection Committee

3

MBM	Multi buoy moorings
MSDS	Material Safety Data Sheet
OCIMF	Oil Companies International Marine Forum
ODME	Oil discharge monitoring equipment
offloading	The process of unloading oil from the FPSO or FSU to the offtake oil tanker.
offtake	The vessel receiving the oil consolidated on board a FPSO or FSU.
oil transfer system	A system which may include pipelines, loading arms, hoses and pumps with accessories designed for pumping oil, dirty ballast and oil residues from a vessel or for delivering cargo oil and bunkers to vessel.
operation	Encompasses loading, discharging or transfer of oil, bunkering, tank washing, discharge of oily residues, and the transfer and storage of dirty ballast.
person in overall advisory control	The person agreed to be in overall advisory control of an STS operation. It may be one of the Masters (generally the Master of the manoeuvring ship) or it may be an STS Superintendent.
PLEM	Pipeline end manifold
responsible person(s)	The person(s) in charge of the operation on the tanker and in charge of the operation on the berth.
Servs	Ship/Response Vessel System
SOPEP	Shipboard Oil Pollution Emergency Plan
ship-to-ship transfer	The transfer of oil cargo from one vessel to another. (Sometimes referred to as "lightening" or "lightering".)
shuttle tanker	A vessel designated for offtake of cargo from a FPSO or a FSU. Such a vessel would normally have a bow loading system and a means of station keeping relative to the FPSO or FSU, without the aid of tugs.
single anchor leg mooring system (SALM)	A mooring facility dedicated to the offshore petroleum discharge system. Once installed, it permits a tanker to remain on station and pump in much higher sea states than is possible with a spread moor.
single point mooring (SPM)	An integrated mooring arrangement for bow mooring a conventional tanker.

SOLAS	International Convention for the Safety of Life at Sea, 1974
SOPEP	Shipboard Oil Pollution Emergency Plan
special areas	As defined in regulation 10 of MARPOL Annex I.
SRS	Ship Reporting System
STCW	International Convention on Standards of Training, Certification and Watchkeeping for Seafarers, 1978
SWL	Safe working load
UNCLOS	United Nations Convention on the Law of the Sea
VRP	Vessel Response Plan
VTMIS	Vessel Traffic Management Information System
VTS	Vessel Traffic Service
WMO	World Meteorological Organization

5

Chapter 1
Introduction

1.1   Prevention of pollution into the marine environment as a consequence of shipping is a primary objective of IMO's work and remains the preferred and most economic means of limiting the introduction of pollutants into the marine environment. A key element in IMO's programme for maritime safety and pollution prevention is the development and implementation of a global regulatory framework designed to enhance safety and to prevent, and eventually eliminate completely, pollution of the marine environment.

1.2   *The International Convention for the Prevention of Pollution from Ships, 1973,* as modified by the Protocol of 1978 relating thereto (MARPOL) is the main international convention aimed at protecting the marine environment from operational and accidental pollution from ships. Its six annexes regulate the prevention of marine pollution by oil; noxious liquid substances in bulk; harmful substances carried by sea in packaged form; sewage; and garbage, as well as the prevention of air pollution.

1.3   In accordance with the provisions of MARPOL, vessels are designed, constructed and operated in an integrated manner, with the objective of preventing and, ultimately, eliminating all harmful discharges and emissions throughout their working life. This holistic philosophy encompasses all vessel operations and their possible impact on the environment, and provides increased opportunities for transport managers to choose environmentally sound sea transport options.

1.4   In recent years, the international maritime transport of oil has grown dramatically. Between 1983 and 2002, world seaborne trade rose from around 12 billion tonne miles to some 23 billion tonne miles, an increase of over 90%. The carriage of oil and petroleum products accounts for a significant part of this increase, rising to approximately 76% from 5.6 billion tonne miles to 9.9 billion tonne miles during this same period. In tonnage terms, the amount of oil transported by sea increased from 1.21 billion tonnes in 1983 to almost 2 billion tonnes in 2002. A total of 33.73 billion tonnes was carried over this 19-year period.

1.5   By contrast, estimates of the quantity of oil spilled during the same period show a steady decline. The introduction of industry practices such as "load on top" and crude oil washing, coupled with segregated ballast requirements for tankers, has contributed significantly towards reducing operational pollution.

1.6   If one considers MARPOL Annex I, the portion of the Convention that covers prevention of pollution by oil, several measures have been introduced to specifically address and lower the element of risk and, more importantly, to ensure oil tankers are constructed and operated in a way that reduces the amount of oil spilled from operational activities or in the event of an incident. This Annex has recently been amended to incorporate more stringent requirements for existing and newly constructed ships, including the phasing-in of double hull requirements for oil tankers; improvements to pump room bottom protection on oil tankers exceeding 5,000 tonnes deadweight; a requirement for double bottoms in pump rooms for vessels constructed on or after 1 January 2007; and more stringent requirements aimed at reducing the accidental outflow of oil in the event of stranding or collision. These measures, together with those requiring protection for bunker tanks on all ships, will significantly reduce the overall risk of oil pollution.

1.7   Correspondingly, important advances have been made in ship and equipment design. Such technological advances, for example, improvements in the design of oily water separating equipment for machinery space bilges and oil tanker discharges, have allowed for stronger international regulations that have effectively reduced the permitted operational discharge of oil effluent from machinery space bilges from 100 parts per million (ppm) to only 15 ppm.

1.8   A greater understanding of spill effects and damages has strengthened the resolve of many governments to focus efforts on prevention. The premise of this manual is that every oil spill, regardless of its size or its source, is worthy of prevention efforts at some level. It is widely understood that the size of an oil spill alone does not determine the degree of its resulting damage – either environmentally or economically. For example, the grounding of the tanker *Jessica* off the Galapagos Islands in 2001 resulted in a relatively small release of oil. However, ongoing studies indicate that this spill is having significant impacts on the endemic marine fauna, demonstrating that even a small spill at a World Heritage Site can have far reaching consequences. As such, the impacts of repeated small operational spills in the confines of a port or along major traffic lanes demand greater attention.

1.9   It is well understood that the most effective means of combating oil pollution is through prevention. Effective prevention includes the proper training of personnel, enforcement of pollution regulations, adopting best practices and enhanced ship construction.

1.10   This manual is intended to provide practical guidance, describing procedures for handling of oil cargoes, bunkering, ship-to-ship transfer operations, transfer operations involving offshore units and operations in ice covered waters. This manual provides a good overview of the various practices to complement the more detailed industry standards and codes of practice currently in place. The information provided does not supersede or replace any information, laws, or regulations contained in any other publications with respect to the waters and areas to which it pertains.

1.11   Prevention should and will remain the fundamental component of any programme to protect the marine environment from accidental spills, recognizing that this does not preclude the need for good preparedness and a timely response to spills when they occur.

Chapter 2
Requirements for all ships

2.1 General

2.1.1 When operations take place that involve loading, discharging or transferring oil, or bunkering or discharging oily mixtures, careful consideration should be given to the issues described in this chapter.

2.1.2 When using the guidance in this part of the manual, due consideration should be given to the requirements of MARPOL Annex I – *Regulations for the prevention of pollution by oil* as amended, in particular, chapters 1, 3 and 5. For application to a particular vessel, the specific regulations in MARPOL Annex I will be applicable.

2.1.3 Account should also be taken of chapter 7 of the *International Safety Management Code* (ISM Code), with respect to the development of plans for shipboard operations. Companies should establish procedures for the preparation of plans and instructions, including checklists as appropriate. The various tasks involved should be defined and assigned to suitably qualified personnel.

2.1.4 Reference should be made to established good industry practices such as those referenced in paragraph 2.9.

2.1.5 Before commencing any operation involving oil or oily mixtures, vessels are required to have been surveyed, certificated, and to have been provided with all statutory documentation relevant to their vessel type and size (e.g. *Shipboard Oil Pollution Emergency Plan, Oil Record Book*, etc.) relevant to such operations.

2.1.6 When at berth or jetty, ships must be securely moored by means of ropes and/or wires that are in good condition and appropriate for the likely applied load. Mooring lines should be regularly inspected. During use, they should be checked to ensure that they are properly tensioned, thereby minimizing any movement of the ship, while taking due account of tidal conditions, etc.

2.1.7   For any operation involving oil or oily mixtures, prior to the commencement of operations, all valves through which oil could be discharged to the sea should be inspected to ensure that they are closed and, if they are intended to be kept closed during the specific operation, they should be secured to ensure that they are not opened.

2.1.8   All scupper holes to which oil would have access in the event of a spillage should be plugged liquid tight for the duration of the operations. Accumulations of water should be periodically drained off the deck and the scupper plugs replaced immediately after the water has been cleared.

2.1.9   If not permanently fitted, drip trays of sufficient size should be placed under hose couplings and flanges before and during operations. These are to be drained or emptied as necessary. Where no facilities exist for the proper drainage of hoses and pipelines, couplings should be suitably blanked immediately on being disconnected.

2.1.10   Dry material, such as sand or oil sorbent, should be available on board vessels to deal with any small spill which may occur. Any oil spilled on deck should be immediately cleaned up and contained for subsequent disposal. Spilled oil should not be washed overboard.

2.1.11   A reliable means of communication should be available throughout oil transfer operations between ship and shore, barge, offshore unit or lightering vessel. Communication should be checked and all signals used should be thoroughly understood by both parties before commencing operations.

2.1.12   Hoses and other equipment to be used should be inspected prior to commencement, and at regular intervals during use, to ensure early detection of leakage or damage. Any hose used for oil transfer should be pressure tested at intervals not exceeding one year. During operations, hoses should be properly connected and supported; with particular care taken to avoid the possibility of their being crushed between ship(s) and quaysides, or between a ship's bottom and the seabed at offshore berths with underwater pipelines. With loading arms, operating personnel should keep a continuous watch to ensure that the arms are free to move with the motion of the ship.

2.1.13   Hoses should be of sufficient length to allow for normal movement of the ship(s), and should not be bent to a radius less than that for which they have been designed.

Figure 1 – *Flexible oil tanker discharge hose to gantry*
(Source OCIMF)

2.1.14   Before attempting to lift any hose on board, responsible officers on board vessels should check that the total weight involved is within the capacity of the relevant ship's derrick or crane.

2.1.15   Where the ambient temperature is below freezing point, pipe joints should not be made with moisture absorbing gasket materials, as these may leak if the pipeline temperature rises.

2.1.16   Where they exist, all side doors to the bunkering stations of a ship should be closed and secured when not in use, and as soon as possible after use.

2.1.17   Advance notice should be sent to any port where a ship is requesting reception facilities for the discharge of oily water residues. In the event that ships experience difficulties in disposal of oily residues due to non-availability of reception facilities, reports to that effect should be made to the flag State Administration for transmission to the IMO (refer to MEPC.1/Circ.469/Rev.1, *Revised Consolidated Format for Reporting Alleged Inadequacies of Port Reception Facilities*).

2.1.18   Due consideration should be given to any regional or national requirements in excess of international obligations as they apply to vessels entering those waters.

2.2   Bunkering operations

2.2.1   Responsible person

2.2.1.1 All bunkering operations on board vessels should be supervised by a responsible person who should be one of the ship's officers. Close co-operation and continuous communication should be maintained between the vessel and shore staff or barge crew throughout the entire bunkering operation

2.2.2   Before bunkering

2.2.2.1 Responsible persons should ensure that all staff engaged in bunkering operations are thoroughly familiar with the ship's fuel system, including the position of overflow and air vent pipes, the overflow tank, the sounding pipes and level indicators.

2.2.2.2 Responsible persons should advise shore staff or barge crew of the maximum rate allowable and also the maximum working pressure on the fuel oil filling lines. They should be aware of the number of tanks that can be filled simultaneously conducive with the maintenance of satisfactory stability conditions. They should know the maximum number of tanks over which proper control can be exercised, and all persons involved in the operation should know the sequence in which the tanks are to be filled.

2.2.2.3 Responsible persons should be satisfied that air vent pipes have been inspected to ensure that displaced air and gases can escape freely and safely.

2.2.2.4 Responsible persons should ensure that accurate soundings or ullages of the oil tanks are taken to determine the quantity of oil already on board and should be satisfied that the expected amount of oil to be delivered can be safely accommodated. They should positively verify the unit of measurement being used with suppliers, e.g. gallons, barrels, tonnes, long or short tons.

2.2.2.5 It is essential that overflow tanks, if fitted, or oil tanks set aside as overflow tanks, are the last to be filled.

2.2.2.6 Valves which are required to be closed should be positively checked and confirmed as closed. Similarly, checks should be made to positively confirm that all valves in the bunker supply lines which are required to be open are open.

2.2.2.7 As well as overfilling of tanks, spillages during bunkering operations due to damaged flexible hoses are another significant cause of pollution. Flexible hoses should be inspected, tested and maintained in accordance with manufacturers' specifications and appropriate regulations.

2.2.2.8 It is recommended that use is made of a *Bunkering Safety Checklist* to confirm that all necessary preloading checks have been carried out and communication systems have been established and tested. An example of a checklist is provided in the appendix.

2.2.3 During bunkering

2.2.3.1 Bunkering should commence slowly so that the supply of fuel can be readily stopped in the event of a mishap. Procedures should be in place to monitor pressure in the supply lines to ensure that maximum working pressures are not exceeded.

2.2.3.2 Frequent soundings or ullages of tanks should be taken. The filling valves of the next tanks in the sequence of filling should be opened before the valves on the tanks being filled are closed. During "topping up" of tanks the delivery rate should be slowed down, and ample warning should be given to the suppliers of the need to reduce the rate of delivery during these operations. Double bottom oil tanks should be "topped up" by gravity, ideally from deep tanks, whenever possible. Filling valves on the ship's bunker lines should not be closed until after the supply has been stopped and the hoses drained.

2.2.4 On completion

2.2.4.1 On completion of bunkering operations, after hoses have been drained, empty drip trays should be left in place below the hose couplings. Flanges should then be separated and blank flanges fitted on the end of filling lines. All fuel line and tank filling valves should be securely closed and a final check of the sounding of all fuel oil tanks should be taken.

2.3 Transferring fuel oil within a ship

2.3.1 When transferring fuel oil within a ship, e.g. from bunker tanks to settling tanks, care should be taken to ensure that any overboard discharge valve from fuel oil transfer pumps is properly closed and secured against accidental discharge. Blank flanges should also be fitted at all times when the overboard discharge line is not in use.

Figure 2 – *Bunkering from bunker barge to ship (Source UNICORN)*

2.3.2 Responsible persons on board vessels should be satisfied that air vent pipes and overflow pipes, where fitted, are clear and in good order. Tank sounding arrangements and/or oil level indicators on settling tanks should not allow the escape of oil in the event of an accidental overfilling of the settling tanks. Frequent soundings or ullages should be taken whilst transfer operations are in progress.

2.4　Machinery space bilges

2.4.1　Machinery space precautions

2.4.1.1 Ships should have the means of preventing fuel oil from escaping into the machinery space bilges. This may be achieved by means of special oil bilges, gutter ways and trays beneath oil pumps, heaters, etc. These arrangements should be regularly inspected and any accumulation of oil should be transferred to a storage tank before the risk of overflow to the ordinary bilges arises. In the case of trays under pumps that do not drain into the oily bilges, these should be kept clean so that any leakage will be immediately apparent and can be dealt with before it can overflow into the ordinary bilges.

2.4.1.2 Consideration should also be given to the prevention of ordinary machinery space bilges overflowing into oily bilges and gutter ways.

15

2.4.1.3 Procedures should be in place requiring regular inspection of oil pressure pipes and fuel oil pipes and fittings to help ensure that any leaks or potential leaks are detected at an early stage and can be dealt with.

2.4.2 Discharge of machinery space bilges

2.4.2.1 Within some defined geographical areas, such as the Antarctic area, any discharge of oil or oily mixtures into the sea from any ship is prohibited.

2.4.2.2 Oil contaminated bilge water shall not be discharged overboard whilst the ship is within 12 nautical miles of a coastal State either directly or through an oily water separator, unless it contains less than 15 ppm of oil and is in compliance with local regulations. Any oil contaminated water, which has accumulated in the machinery space bilges prior to arrival and while a vessel is in port should, if possible, be disposed of at shore facilities before the vessel sails. A standard discharge connection in accordance with the requirements of regulation 13 of MARPOL Annex I should be provided to facilitate the disposal to reception facilities of any accumulation of oily bilge water.

2.4.2.3 If no shore reception facilities exist, bilges should be pumped into a suitable storage tank, for subsequent disposal, through the oily water separator in accordance with the requirements of relevant regulations. Reference should be made to paragraph 2.1.17 for information regarding the reporting of the inadequacy or non-availability of reception facilities.

2.4.2.4 Any discharge into the sea of oil or oily mixture from a ship of less than 400 gross tonnage is prohibited, except when all of the following conditions are satisfied:

.1 the ship is proceeding en route;

.2 the ship has in operation equipment of a design approved by the administration that ensures that the oil content of the effluent without dilution does not exceed 15 ppm;

.3 the oily mixture does not originate from cargo pump room bilges on oil tankers;

.4 the oily mixture, in the case of oil tankers, is not mixed with oil cargo residues; and

.5 the vessel is not within the Antarctic area.

2.4.2.5 In a special area,* any discharge into the sea of oil or oily mixtures from ships of 400 gross tonnage and above is prohibited, except when all of the following conditions are satisfied:

.1   the ship is proceeding en route;

.2   the oily mixture is processed through oil filtering equipment that meets the requirements of regulation 14.7 of MARPOL Annex I;

.3   the oil content of the effluent without dilution does not exceed 15 ppm;

.4   the oily mixture does not originate from cargo pump room bilges on oil tankers;

.5   oily mixture, in the case of oil tankers, is not mixed with oil cargo residues; and

.6   the vessel is not within the Antarctic area.

2.4.2.6 Outside special areas, any discharge into the sea of oil or oily mixtures from ships of 400 gross tonnage and above is prohibited, except when all of the following conditions are satisfied:

.1   the ship is proceeding en route;

.2   the oily mixture is processed through oil filtering equipment that meets the requirements of regulation 14 of MARPOL Annex I;

.3   the oil content of the effluent without dilution does not exceed 15 ppm;

.4   the oily mixture does not originate from cargo pump room bilges on oil tankers;

.5   the oily mixture, in the case of oil tankers, is not mixed with oil cargo residues; and

.6   the vessel is not within the Antarctic area.

---

* A "special area" means a sea area where, for recognized technical reasons in relation to its oceanographical and ecological condition and to the particular character of its traffic, the adoption of special mandatory methods for the prevention of sea pollution by oil is required. For the purposes of MARPOL Annex I, the special areas are defined in chapter 1, regulation 1.

2.5 Oily water separating equipment and oil content meters

2.5.1 The design, construction and operation of these items is to be in accordance with guidelines produced by the Organization.

2.5.2 Operating procedures for this equipment will vary from one make to another, and manufacturer's instructions should be readily available on board ships and should be strictly observed. The equipment should always be maintained in good working order.

2.5.3 Close attention should be paid to the rate of pumping when the equipment is in operation. Pumping in excess of the manufacturer's rated throughput is the most common cause of excessive oil content in the effluent to be discharged. Although the maximum throughput of the system as rated by the manufacturer may be used initially for effluent with relatively low contamination, pumping rates should, if possible, be reduced for more heavily contaminated effluent.

2.5.4 Detergents should not be used to clean bilges and/or fuel oil tanks if the washings are to be discharged through oily water separating equipment or oil filtering equipment, unless such detergents are specifically approved.

2.5.5 When oil contaminated water is passed through an oily water separator, the recovered oil residues should be retained and transferred to storage tanks until they can be disposed of at reception facilities, burnt in boilers or incinerated.

2.6 Fuel and lubricating oil purifiers

2.6.1 Every ship of 400 gross tonnage and above shall be provided with sludge tank(s) to receive oil residues such as those resulting from the purification of fuel and lubricating oils.

2.7 Oil Record Book

2.7.1 Every oil tanker of 150 gross tonnage or above and every ship of 400 gross tonnage and above, other than an oil tanker, must be provided with *Oil Record Book(s)*.

2.7.2 Loading and unloading of oil cargo, discharge of oily waste, handling of ballast water and/or internal transfer of oil cargo operations must be recorded in the *Oil Record Book*.

2.8   Checklists

2.8.1   Checklists, where relevant, should be specified by company procedures. Operations that may benefit from the provisions of such checklists include:

.1   bunkering;

.2   loading;

.3   discharging;

.4   transfer of oil cargo; and

.5   lightering.

Examples of checklists covering the aforementioned activities are included in the appendix.

2.8.2   If printed checklists are used, the procedures should include a requirement that they are to be completed at the appropriate time and verified by the responsible person.

2.8.3   The development of vessel and operation specific procedures and checklists should take account of available industry guidance and best practice.

2.9   References

International Convention for the Prevention of Pollution from Ships, 1973, as modified by the Protocol of 1978 relating thereto (MARPOL) – (IMO)

International Safety Management Code (ISM Code) – (IMO)

Mooring equipment guidelines – (OCIMF)

United States Clean Water Act & Environmental Protection Agency Permit for Commercial Vessels – www.epa.gov/npdes/vessels

Guidelines for the development of shipboard oil pollution emergency plans – IMO MEPC resolution MEPC.54(32) as amended by resolution MEPC.86(44) – (IMO)

Form of Oil Record Book – MARPOL Annex I, appendix III – (IMO)

Recommendation on international performance and test specification for oily water separating equipment and oil content meters – IMO Assembly resolution A.393(X) – (IMO)

19

Guidelines and specifications for pollution prevention equipment for machinery space bilges of ships – IMO MEPC resolution MEPC.60(33) – (IMO)

Revised guidelines and specifications for pollution prevention equipment for machinery space bilges of ships – IMO MEPC resolution MEPC.107(49) – (IMO)

A guide for correct entries in the Oil Record Book (Part I – Machinery space operations) – (INTERTANKO)

2.10 Relevant industry websites

International Chamber of Shipping (ICS)	www.marisec.org
International Association of Independent Tanker Owners (INTERTANKO)	www.intertanko.com
Oil Companies International Marine Forum (OCIMF)	www.ocimf.com
International Association of Dry Cargo Shipowners (INTERCARGO)	www.intercargo.co.uk
The Baltic and International Maritime Council (BIMCO)	www.bimco.org
Cruise Lines International Association (CLIA)	www.cruising.org
International Parcel Tankers Association (IPTA)	www.ipta.org.uk

Chapter 3
Requirements for all tankers

3.1   General application of MARPOL Annex I

3.1.1   In addition to the information contained in chapter 1, and to supplement the precautions to be observed listed under chapter 2.1, this chapter addresses certain design requirements and the additional precautions necessary in the case of oil tankers. MARPOL includes certain regulations for tankers, which are outlined in the following paragraphs. For the full meaning of the relevant regulation, it is recommended that the full text of the specific regulation is referred to, and as subsequently amended.

3.1.2   Chapter 4 of MARPOL Annex I contains *Requirements for the cargo areas of oil tankers*. This chapter contains a series of regulations subdivided into three parts with Part A addressing *Construction* details, Part B addressing *Equipment* requirements and Part C relating to the *Control of operational discharge of oil*. These regulations closely determine the scope of an oil tanker's operational methods for ballast and cargo handling.

3.1.3   All regulations identified in this section refer to MARPOL Annex I, unless otherwise indicated.

3.2   Oil tanker operations

3.2.1   General

3.2.1.1   Due to the differences in crude oil and product tanker operations, which mainly relate to their respective tank cleaning methods, this section has been subdivided into subsections A and B in order to specifically address these differing operations. Subsection A addresses crude oil tanker operations from an oil pollution prevention perspective, whereas subsection B addresses operations on product tankers.

A   Crude oil tankers

3.2.2   Ballast voyage procedures

3.2.2.1 For a ballast passage, adequate segregated ballast will have been loaded at the previous discharge port to meet the requirements

21

of regulation 18 with respect to the ship's draft and trim requirements. Prior to discharge of this segregated ballast water at the subsequent loading port, the following sequence of procedures should be observed:

.1   a visual examination of the ballast water for any oil or oil traces on its surface should be undertaken (regulation 30.6.1). In the event that oil or oil traces are seen, the discharge procedures, as set out in paragraph 3.2.3.1 onwards, for water containing oily traces, are to be followed; and

.2   it should be ensured that the segregated ballast water for discharge complies with the requirements contained in the Ballast Water Management plan for the vessel.

3.2.2.2 In the rare and exceptional event (regulation 18.3 and Unified Interpretations 26.1) that additional water ballast is loaded into a cargo tank, then the loading, processing and discharge of this water shall be in compliance with regulation 34 and the following sequence of procedures shall be observed:

.1   prior to loading any ballast water in a cargo tank, the tank has to have been crude oil washed (regulation 18.4) at the previous discharge port;

.2   it should be ensured that all sea chest, pipeline and tank valves are closed;

.3   where necessary for tankers with only a sea chest for the segregated ballast water pipeline system, the spool piece between the segregated ballast water pipeline system and the crude oil cargo pipeline system should be inserted;

.4   the inboard pipeline system to the designated cargo tank/s should be opened;

.5   the necessary cargo pump should be started before slowly opening the sea chest valve, whilst simultaneously monitoring a vacuum created by the pump as registered on the pump pressure gauge. To prevent oil from leaking overboard by way of the sea suction when commencing to take on ballast, pump room, line and tank valves are to be properly set and the pumps are to be running with a vacuum established on the sea line before the sea valves are opened. In order to establish this initial vacuum on the sea line, it may be necessary to take particular precautions, such as bleeding gas from the pump housing and utilizing a stripping pump or vacuum systems on the vapour line located at the top of the pump housing, where such are available;

.6   when ballasting is completed, the sea chest valve should be closed before stopping the pump. Thereafter, it should be ensured that all valves in the pipeline system that have been used are closed;

.7   discharge of this ballast water shall be undertaken by complying with regulations 30.1, 30.2, 30.6.4 and 34;

.8   once the oil/water interface measurement has been established by use of the oil/water interface detector (regulation 32), gravity discharge to the sea can be undertaken, subject to compliance with the operational and geographic limitation requirements of regulation 34;

.9   when the oil/water interface is approached, gravity discharge is to be immediately stopped and the remaining ballast water should be transferred to the slop tanks (regulation 29) for continued discharge through the oil discharge monitoring equipment (ODME) (regulation 31) and in compliance with regulation 34;

.10   once the remainder of the ballast water is transferred to the slop tank, a settling period should be allowed so that the oil/water interface is re-established. This interface has to be measured before resumed discharge through the ODME is allowed;

.11   resumption of discharge of the ballast water through the ODME is undertaken at two differing rates of discharge; the initial rate of cleaner ballast water at a higher rate and reported in the *Oil Record Book*, Part II under section (I) 47, whereas the more polluted water closer to the interface is discharged at a slower rate and reported in (I) 48;

.12   on completion of this process, any retained quantity of oil and water in the slop tanks may either be loaded on top with the next crude oil cargo or delivered ashore to a Reception Facility (regulation 38); and

.13   each phase of these ballasting/deballasting operations will be recorded in the *Oil Record Book*, Part II, as required by regulation 36.

3.2.3 Crude oil cargo discharge and pipeline draining

3.2.3.1 During the discharge of a crude oil tanker's cargo, crude oil washing of the tanks may be undertaken simultaneously with the discharge. This washing process and system, which is often referred to as "COW", is fully described in the IMO publication *Crude oil washing systems*. A crude oil tanker fitted with fixed washing equipment in the tanks directly connected to the cargo pumping system can use crude oil instead of water as a washing medium. Every crude oil tanker operating with a crude oil washing system, in accordance with regulations 33 and 35, must be provided with a *Crude Oil Washing Operations and Equipment Manual* detailing the procedures to be followed in operating the tanker with COW, developed particularly for the tanker and approved by the administration. The crude oil, if suitable, when used as a washing medium, dissolves the oil clingage and deposits in the cargo tanks so that these residues may be discharged with the cargo, rendering the tanks freer of liquid and solid residues.

3.2.3.2 When it is required to carry out crude oil washing, the responsible person should have compiled a crude oil washing plan (as integrated into the tanker's discharge plan) and notified the berth representative to this effect. Such crude oil washing operations may be subject to in-port inspection in accordance with the *guidelines for in-port inspection of crude oil washing procedures* which are included in the IMO publication *Crude oil washing systems*. If, for any reason, permission to crude oil wash is refused, this should be reported to the flag State Administration for onward transmission to IMO and the oil tanker should take such alternative measures as prescribed by the port State Administration.

3.2.3.3 Before arrival in port, a check is made to ensure that the valves on all washing machines are securely shut. The tank washing system should be pressure tested and examined for leaks. While crude oil washing is in progress, the system must be kept under continuous observation so that any leak will be detected immediately and action can be taken to deal with it. On completion of washing, the system must be completely drained of oil.

3.2.3.4 No part of the crude oil washing system shall enter the machinery spaces. Where the tank washing system is fitted with a steam heater for use when water washing, the heater must be effectively isolated during crude oil washing by double shut-off valves or by clearly identifiable blanks.

3.2.3.5 During crude oil washing, hydrocarbon gas is generated within the tanks. Cargo tanks must be rendered inert prior to and during crude oil washing operations. The entry of inert gas should be controlled so that a positive pressure is maintained at all times below the level at which the pressure/

vacuum relief valves operate. By this means, both the venting of hydrocarbon gas from the tank and the entry of air from outside the tanks are prevented. If this over pressure cannot be maintained or the oxygen quality of the inert gas phase exceeds 8% in the cargo tanks, then the operation is to be immediately suspended until the required conditions are restored for safe operation.

3.2.3.6 A notice should be displayed in the cargo and engine control rooms, on the bridge and on the noticeboards of oil tankers, which use crude oil washing. The following wording is suggested:

THE TANK WASHING LINES ON THIS SHIP MAY CONTAIN
CRUDE OIL. ON NO ACCOUNT ARE VALVES ON THESE LINES
TO BE OPENED BY UNAUTHORIZED PERSONNEL.

3.2.3.7 All crude oil washing operations should be entered in the *Oil Record Book*, Part II, Section D.

3.2.3.8 Upon completion of discharge of a crude oil cargo, all lines containing cargo should be stripped to shore using a smaller diameter pipeline and cargo stripping pump (regulation 30.4). This pipeline, often referred to as the "MARPOL pipeline" ensures that only a limited quantity of cargo remains within the main cargo pipeline system on board on completion of discharge. This operation includes opening pump bypass lines and cross connections between cargo and stripping lines. Any remaining cargo in the pipelines that cannot be pumped ashore should be drained into a separate tank or into the slop tank before ballasting begins.

3.2.3.9 To prevent oil from leaking overboard, by way of a sea chest connected to the cargo pipeline system crossover in the pump room, when undertaking cargo operations, it is essential that the sea chest valve and its inboard isolation valve are fully closed. A functioning *positive means* must be installed in the pipeline system in order to prevent the section of pipeline between the sea chest valve and the inboard valve being filled with cargo.

3.2.4   Tank washing

3.2.4.1 During the ballast voyage, it may be necessary for cargo tanks to be washed to achieve a gas free state for tank inspection and entry. Should such an operation be undertaken, the relevant tank(s) should be washed as required and are to be suitably blanketed with inert gas containing less than 8% oxygen, with washings being continuously stripped or educted to the slop tank. Care should be taken to ensure that wash water does not build up in the cargo tank as this impacts on the effectiveness of the wash. Furthermore, it is essential that the slop tank(s) is continuously monitored so as to prevent overfilling. It should be understood that the quantity of oil eventually discharged to the sea can be minimized by eliminating unnecessary washing, thus reducing the total quantity of water requiring treatment and processing that is brought into contact with oil within the tanker.

3.2.4.2 For discharge of the wash water from the slop tank, the treatment and processing required is similar to that specified in paragraphs 3.2.2.2.10 to 3.2.2.2.13. Normally, a crude oil tanker will be equipped with two slop tanks that are directly connected to one another with a pipeline and isolation valve. This arrangement is used for decanting and separation of water from free oil. The time required for oil and water to separate in the slop tank depends upon the motion of the ship, as well as on the type of previous cargo. Under favourable conditions, a few hours may be enough, but in most circumstances 36 hours or more should be allowed.

3.2.4.3 The tank wash water together with recovered oil, sediment and sludge, is stripped, by pump or eductor, from the tank being washed into the first slop tank where primary separation of oil and water takes place. The "dirty" water phase in the first slop tank is then decanted to the second slop tank for further separation before being discharged overboard. Before starting the overboard discharge, an accurate interface and ullage reading, using an oil/water interface detector, must be taken to determine the depth of the oil layer. Certain products may accumulate an electrostatic charge, which must be allowed to dissipate before taking interface readings. Accordingly, strict adherence to internationally accepted safety precautions covering ullage and sampling is essential. The content of the second slop tanks can thereafter be discharged at the varying rates, as described above in paragraph 3.2.2.2.11 but through the ODME to control the oil content being discharged in compliance with regulation 34.

3.2.4.4 The procedure for slop tank discharge overboard can be summarized as follows:

.1 pump down the slop tank using one main cargo pump at slow speed until a water depth of about 20% of the tank is reached;

.2 stop the cargo pump, take an oil/water interface and ullage reading and recalculate the remaining water depth;

.3 resume pumping of the slop tank, this time using the stripping system, until a predetermined water depth is reached which, for the particular size and construction of the slop tank, is known not to give rise to discharge of oil. Pumping, which may initially be at a moderate rate, should be slowed as this predetermined water depth is approached;

.4   if oil should appear before the predetermined water depth is reached or the monitor indicates that the oil content of the effluent discharged approaches the permitted limits, stop pumping; and

.5   allow further settling of the slop tank contents for as long as possible before repeating steps .3 and .4.

This total procedure should be promptly recorded in Sections G and I of the *Oil Record Book*, Part II, as appropriate.

3.2.4.5 Slop tank discharges cannot be undertaken in designated special areas, as specified in regulation 1.11.

3.2.5   Disposal of slop residues

3.2.5.1 Before reaching the loading port, the Master should advise his owners or charterers of the amount of retained residues on board. These may then be handled in one of the following ways:

.1   by pumping the residues ashore at the loading terminal;

.2   by retaining the residues on board and loading the new cargo on top of them; or

.3   by retaining the residues on board, but segregated from the new cargo. If this is done, it may be possible to pump them ashore at the unloading terminal, if reception facilities are available. It may, however, be necessary to retain the residues for more than one voyage.

B   Product tankers

3.2.6   General

3.2.6.1 As stated in paragraph 3.2.1.1, activities associated with the cargo operations of a product tanker differ from a crude oil tanker due to their differing methods of tank cleaning. Whereas crude oil tankers mainly use COW for the washing of their cargo tanks, product tankers will use sea or fresh water for this purpose and may occasionally use a chemical additive to enhance the effectiveness of the cleaning operation. Given these differences, this section concentrates on product tanker tank cleaning procedures and wash water disposal or discharge.

3.2.7   Cargo and ballast pipeline systems

3.2.7.1 Product tankers will normally carry several differing parcels and grades of oil product simultaneously. This necessitates the installation on board the tanker of a more complex but flexible cargo pipeline system that is capable of loading and discharging these parcels and grades of oil product simultaneously but totally segregated from one another to or from their designated manifold connection to the shore facility. This is achieved by use of double valve separation between individual pipeline systems on board or the installation of individual tank loading and discharge systems and the use of deep well pumps in each tank.

3.2.7.2 As required by regulation 18, the segregated ballast water pipeline system is totally separated from the cargo pipeline systems on board but connection between the two systems can be achieved by insertion of a spool piece or the removal of a "positive" blank flange between the systems.

3.2.8   Ballast voyage procedures

3.2.8.1 Pursuant to the requirements of regulation 18, a Product tanker will be constructed with a double hull and adequate segregated ballast capacity. For a ballast passage, adequate segregated ballast should have been loaded at the previous discharge port to meet the requirements of regulation 18 with respect to the ship's draft and trim requirements. Prior to discharge of this segregated ballast water at a subsequent loading port, the following sequence of procedures should be observed:

.1   a visual examination of the ballast water should be undertaken to determine any oil or oil traces on its surface (regulation 30.6.1). In the event that oil or oil traces are seen, then the discharge procedures, as set out in paragraph 3.2.2.2.7 and onwards, for water containing oily traces, are to be followed; and

.2   it should be ensured that the segregated ballast water for discharge complies with the requirements contained in the Ballast Water Management plan for the vessel.

3.2.9   Sea water washing of cargo tanks and wash water disposal

3.2.9.1 During the ballast voyage, it may be necessary for the cargo tanks to be washed in order to prepare them for the next cargo to be loaded. Should such an operation be undertaken, the relevant tank(s) will be washed with sea or fresh water, as appropriate. If the product tanker is above 20,000 tonnes DWT, the tanks will be suitably blanketed with inert gas containing less than 8% oxygen. Tank washings will be continuously stripped or educted to a slop tank. Care should be taken to ensure that wash water does not build up in the cargo tank as this affects the effectiveness of the wash. It is essential that the slop tank(s) is continuously monitored so as to prevent overfilling. It should be understood that the quantity of oil eventually discharged to the sea can be minimized by eliminating unnecessary washing, thus reducing the total quantity of water requiring treatment and processing that is brought into contact with oil within the product tanker.

3.2.9.2 Normally a product tanker will be equipped with two slop tanks that are directly connected to one another with a pipeline and isolation valve. This arrangement, which acts as a form of "weir" for separation purposes, is used for decanting and separation of water from free oil. The time required for oil and water to separate in the slop tank depends upon the motion of the ship, as well as on the type of previous cargo. Under favourable conditions, a few hours may be enough but in most circumstances 36 hours or more should be allowed, especially for heavier product cargoes such as fuel oil.

3.2.9.3 The tank wash water and recovered oil, sediment and sludge are stripped, by pump or eductor, from the tank being washed into the first slop tank where primary separation of oil and water takes place. The "dirty" water phase in the first slop tank is then decanted to the second slop tank for further separation before being discharged overboard. Before starting the overboard discharge, an accurate interface and ullage reading, using an oil/water interface detector, must be taken to determine the depth of the oil layer. Certain products may accumulate an electrostatic charge, which must be allowed to dissipate before taking interface readings. Accordingly, strict adherence to internationally accepted safety precautions covering ullage and sampling is essential. The content of the second slop tank can thereafter be discharged at the varying rates through the ODME. The discharge of the water through the ODME is undertaken at two differing rates of discharge; the initial rate of cleaner water, furthest from the oil/water interface, can be undertaken at a higher rate and reported in the *Oil Record Book*, Part II under section (I) 47, whereas the more polluted water closer to the interface is discharged at a slower rate and reported in Section (I) 48 of the *Oil Record Book*, Part II. The ODME will control the oil content of the water being discharged in compliance with regulation 34.

3.2.9.4 The treatment and processing to be used for the discharge of the tank cleaning wash water overboard from the slop tank(s) is summarized as follows:

.1   pump down the slop tank using one main cargo pump at slow speed until a water depth of about 20% of the tank is reached;

.2 stop the cargo pump, than take an oil/water interface and ullage reading and recalculate the remaining water depth;

.3 resume pumping of the slop tank, this time using the stripping system, until a predetermined water depth is reached which, for the particular size and construction of the slop tank, is known not to give rise to discharge of oil. Pumping, which may initially be at a moderate rate, should be slowed as this predetermined water depth is approached;

.4 if oil should appear before the predetermined water depth is reached or the monitor indicates that the oil content of the effluent discharged approaches the permitted limits, stop pumping; and

.5 allow further settling of the slop tank contents for as long as possible before repeating steps .3 and .4.

The above procedure should be promptly recorded in Sections (G) and (I) of the *Oil Record Book,* Part II, as appropriate.

3.2.9.5 Slop tank discharges cannot be undertaken in designated special areas as specified in regulation 1.11 or if the water contains any tank washing chemical additive (regulation 34.8). In such cases, the cargo tank washing water contained in the slop tanks has to be delivered to a reception facility in compliance with regulation 34.9.

3.3   References

The International Convention for the Prevention of Pollution from Ships, 1973, as modified by the Protocol of 1978 relating thereto (MARPOL) – (IMO)

Form of Oil Record Book – MARPOL Annex I, appendix III – (IMO)

Recommendation on international performance and test specification for oily water separating equipment and oil content meters – IMO Assembly resolution A.393 (X) – (IMO)

A guide for correct entries in the Oil Record Book (Part I – Machinery space operations) – (INTERTANKO)

A guide to crude oil washing and cargo heating criteria – (INTERTANKO)

Crude oil washing systems – (IMO)

Chapter 4
Oil tanker operations at berths, piers or jetties

4.1 General

4.1.1 The loading or discharging of an oil tanker is conducted by connecting hoses, or loading arms, between the fixed end of the facility pipeline and the cargo manifold on board the oil tanker in such a way as to permit the transfer of oil without leakage. The operation should always be controlled so as to prevent any escape or spillage of oil.

4.1.2 The transfer of oil, by its nature, involves a potential for pollution and there are many factors that may result in pollution including:

.1 equipment failure;

.2 design faults;

.3 human error;

.4 inadequate training; and

.5 environmental conditions.

To prevent pollution, every practicable precaution regarding the operation should be taken and a contingency plan should be prepared to deal with emergencies, which may occur. This contingency plan should be tested at regular intervals by means of exercises, which should highlight any weaknesses.

4.1.3 The following basic principles should be applied if pollution is to be avoided:

.1 all personnel on the oil tanker and berth connected with the loading or discharge of oil should be fully aware of the need to prevent pollution;

.2 all personnel should be familiar with the content of the respective oil transfer procedures for the facility or the oil tanker and related accepted industry codes of practice, such as those contained in the *International safety guide for oil tankers and terminals*;

31

.3   all personnel should adhere strictly to the joint plan of operation, including the provision of an efficient communication system;

.4   the responsible persons on the oil tanker and the berth should check the items listed in paragraph 4.5.5 before the oil actually flows;

.5   all personnel involved should be familiar with the content of emergency plans, including those for oil spill, and be aware of the immediate measures and response necessary in the event of an escape of oil; and

.6   all equipment, the failure of which might result in an escape of oil, should be inspected and tested regularly.

4.2   Requirements for berths

4.2.1   The location and orientation of the berth should exclude or minimize the dangerous influence of open sea conditions, strong currents and other factors, which may complicate mooring and cause excessive movement of the oil tanker at the berth. The water depth should be sufficient to ensure that all oil tankers handled will remain afloat at all times.

4.2.2   The berth should be designed to prevent unintended accumulations of oil. The containment facilities provided at the berth should be sized for an appropriate containment volume following a realistic risk assessment.

4.2.3   Each berth should be equipped with mooring equipment and fendering arrangements appropriate for the sizes of oil tanker using the berth. The equipment provided should allow the ship's mooring arrangements to hold the ship securely alongside the berth in the maximum weather and tidal conditions established for safe operations.

4.3   Requirements for facilities

4.3.1   Loading arms

4.3.1.1   The material and design of the loading arms should be compatible with the transferred cargo, suitable for local meteorological conditions and possess a sufficient safety margin to allow for the dynamic load exerted by the oil tanker. The loading arms should meet the design and construction requirements for oil transfer systems approved by the appropriate authorities.

Figure 3 – *Hard loading arms connected to the ship's manifolds*
(Source OCIMF)

4.3.1.2 Loading arms should have a designed operating envelope to enable free movement to take account of the following:

.1 tidal range at the berth;

.2 maximum and minimum freeboards of the largest and smallest oil tankers for which the berth has been designed;

.3 minimum and maximum oil tanker manifold setbacks from the deck edge;

.4 changes in horizontal position due to tanker thwartship drift and ranging; and

.5 maximum and minimum spacing when operating with other arms in a bank.

4.3.1.3 The limits of the loading arm's operating envelope should be fully understood by berth operators. The installations should include a visual indication of the operating envelope and/or be provided with alarms to indicate excessive range and drift.

4.3.1.4 Terminal procedures should address actions to be taken to keep the oil tanker's manifold within the operating envelope during all stages of the transfer operation and, should this not be possible, should require the immediate suspension of operations and disconnection of the loading arm(s).

4.3.1.5 Loading arms should be properly rigged and, where necessary, measures should be taken to ensure that excessive forces are not placed on the oil tanker's manifold. This may be achieved by the use of supports or jacks.

4.3.1.6 Each loading arm should be equipped with a means to facilitate oil drainage or an arrangement for preventing oil spillage, prior to connecting or when disconnecting the arm.

4.3.1.7 Each loading arm should be fitted with an insulating flange to prevent electrical flow between an oil tanker and the berth during connection or disconnection. The insulating flange should be inspected and tested at least annually.

4.3.1.8 Loading arms, together with associated valves and couplings, should be periodically pressure tested in accordance with manufacturer's recommendations. The results of the tests should be documented and maintained at the facility.

4.3.2   Hoses

4.3.2.1 Hoses should be manufactured and tested in accordance with a recognized international standard and should be of a grade and type suitable for the service and operating conditions in which they are to be used.

4.3.2.2 Hoses are classified according to their "rated working pressure" and this pressure should not be exceeded in service. The "rated working pressure" is equal to and the same as the "maximum working pressure", the "maximum allowable working pressure" and the "factory test pressure" and any one of these terms may be used by differing organizations.

4.3.2.3 Hoses used for the transfer of oil, dirty ballast or bunkers should have a minimum burst test pressure that is at least four times the "rated working pressure".

4.3.2.4 Each hose should bear the following durable indelible markings:

.1   the manufacturer's name or trademark;

.2   identification of the standard specification for manufacture;

.3   factory test pressure (note: equal to rated working pressure, maximum working pressure, maximum allowable working pressure);

.4   month and year of manufacture and manufacturer's serial number;

.5   indication that the hose is electrically continuous or electrically discontinuous, semi-continuous or anti-static; and

.6   the type of service for which it is intended, e.g. oil or chemical.

4.3.2.5 Hoses in service should have a documented inspection at least annually to confirm their suitability for continued use. This should include:

.1   a thorough visual check for deterioration or damage;

.2   a pressure test to a pressure defined by local requirements or as recommended by industry codes of practice. For example, the *International safety guide for oil tankers and terminals (ISGOTT)* recommends a test pressure of 1.5 times the rated working pressure to check for leakage or movement of end fittings; and

.3   an electrical continuity test.

Records of the results of the routine inspections with respect to each hose should be available at the facility.

4.3.2.6 Hoses should be withdrawn from service and retired against defined criteria, which may include the following:

.1   the presence of defects detected during visual inspections. Defects prompting retirement could include irregularities in the outside diameter, such as kinking, damaged or exposed reinforcement or permanent deformation of the casing and damage, slippage or misalignment of end fittings;

.2   after a defined period in service, established in consultation with the manufacturer; and

.3   when the temporary elongation of the hose, measured during the routine pressure test, exceeds maximum allowable values.

4.3.2.7 A visual inspection of each of the hose assemblies should be carried out before they are connected to the oil tanker's manifold to determine that they are free of damage. If damage to a hose or flange is present, the hose should be withdrawn from use for further inspection, repair or retirement.

4.3.2.8 Measures should be taken to prevent electrical flow between the oil tanker and the berth during connection or disconnection of the hose assembly by including an insulating flange at the shore connection. Alternatively, a single length of non conducting hose may be included within each hose assembly. The insulating arrangements should be inspected and tested at least annually. The use of a ship/shore bonding cable may be dangerous and is not recommended.

4.3.2.9 Hoses should be properly suspended and supported throughout the transfer operation by the use of lifting bridles and saddles. Measures should be taken to ensure that hoses are not bent to a radius smaller than their minimum bend radius specified by the manufacturer.

4.3.2.10 Depending on their design, the elements of each hose assembly should meet the following requirements:

.1   threaded couplings should ensure the security of connection without any additional fixing arrangements;

.2   flanged joints should meet the requirements of international standards for connecting sizes, and their material and design should correspond to accepted standards; and

.3   quick release couplings should meet the requirements of international standards for connecting sizes. Their material and design should correspond to accepted standards.

4.4   Control and communications

4.4.1   The control centre for the operation should be equipped with all the means required to effectively control the operations, including means for emergency stopping of the oil flow.

4.4.2   In the area of each facility, there should be a post for control of the operation on the berth, which meets the following requirements:

.1   secure protection of equipment and personnel from rain, snow and water spray during rough seas and wind, and protection from oil in case of failure of loading arms and hoses; and

.2   good view of the berth, the position of the loading arms and/ or hoses and the movements of the oil tanker.

4.4.3   Supervision should be aimed at preventing hazardous situations developing, which may require a competent member of the shore organization to be on continuous duty in the vicinity of the ship-to-shore connections.

4.4.4   Subject to the results of a formal risk assessment, and if local regulations permit, terminal operators may consider reducing manning at the berth or de-man the berth during non critical phases of the cargo transfer operation. In such circumstances the ship/shore connections should remain under continual observation by remote means, and effective control over cargo operations must be retained. The responsible person on the berth and on board the oil tanker should periodically check the following and, if necessary, take appropriate remedial action:

.1   for any leakage from the equipment and system, or through the oil tanker's plating;

.2   that there is no leakage into pump rooms, ballast or void spaces or cargo tanks not scheduled to be loaded;

.3   if there is any excessive pressure in piping and hoses;

.4   the mooring arrangements;

.5   the condition of loading arms and hoses and their support arrangements; and

.6   tank ullages and quantities transferred.

4.4.5   Each facility should be equipped with a radio and/or telephone ensuring reliable two-way communications by voice between the responsible person on the berth or in the control centre and the responsible person on the oil tanker. The communications shall be in an agreed language, understood by both persons.

4.4.6   Each facility should be equipped with a reliable means for two-way communication with the operator(s) at the storage tanks in use. This communication link should allow for operational parameters to be changed quickly and efficiently and for immediate pump shut-off in the case of an emergency.

4.4.7   Emergency shutdown of operations

4.4.7.1   A documented emergency shutdown procedure, including details of emergency alarms, should be agreed by the responsible persons during the pre-transfer discussions. The procedure should include details of the following:

.1   the means of raising the alarm in the event of an emergency;

.2   the means of stopping transfer within the facility, including the location and mode of operation of shut-off devices;

.3   the means of stopping transfer on board the oil tanker, including the location and method of operation of shut-off devices; and

.4   if applicable, the method of operating any shut-off devices that are connected to the oil tanker and facility by electrical, pneumatic or mechanical means.

4.4.7.2 Due regard must be given to the possible dangers of a pressure surge associated with the emergency shutdown procedure, which could result in the rupture of pipelines or hoses. This risk may be reduced by measures that include the effective control of flow rates, ensuring that motorized valves do not close too quickly and by the use of pressure relieving arrangements in the transfer system.

4.4.8   Illumination

4.4.8.1 The facility should have a level of illumination sufficient to ensure that all ship/shore interface activities can be safely conducted during periods of darkness. In particular, a permanently installed illumination system should ensure proper illumination of:

.1   berth working areas;

.2   each coupling of loading arms or hoses with the shore piping systems and oil tanker manifolds;

.3   gangways between berth and oil tanker;

.4   access and emergency escape routes;

.5   mooring dolphins and walkways;

.6   each area of the facility, within which oil transfer operations are performed;

.7   valves for the control of the piping systems; and

.8   shut-off switches for emergency stopping of the transfer operation.

4.4.8.2 Illumination levels in the locations listed above should, as a minimum, meet national or international standards.

4.5   Preparation for operations

4.5.1   The Master of an oil tanker should be fully advised of the availability of tugs and mooring craft and of any particular features of the berth. He should also be advised regarding any local regulations and potential penalties for any infringement regarding marine pollution.

4.5.2   A joint plan of operation should be developed on the basis of information exchanged between the oil tanker and the facility, comprising the following:

.1   mooring arrangements;

.2   quantities and characteristics of the cargo(es) to be loaded (discharged) and identification of any toxic components;

.3   sequence of loading (discharging) of tanks;

.4   details of cargo transfer system, number of pumps and maximum permissible pressure;

.5   rate of oil transfer during operations (initial, maximum and topping-up);

.6   the time required for starting, stopping and changing rate of delivery during topping-off of tanks;

.7   normal stopping and emergency shutdown procedures;

.8   disposition and quantity of ballast and slops, and disposal if applicable;

.9   maximum draught and freeboard anticipated during operation;

.10   details of proposed method of venting or inerting cargo tanks;

.11   details of crude oil washing, if applicable;

.12   emergency and oil spill containment procedures;

.13   sequence of actions in case of spillage of oil;

.14   environmental and operational limits that would trigger suspension of the transfer operation, disconnection of hoses, and removal of the oil tanker from the berth;

.15   specific conditions of operations (if any); and

.16   local or government rules that apply to the transfer.

4.5.3   Loading arms should be aligned with oil tanker pipelines and the responsible person(s) advised of any constraints on ship movement imposed by their use.

4.5.4   Hoses should be suspended in such a way that the possibility of twisting and pinching between the berth and the oil tanker, bending to a radius less than their minimum bending radius, and abrasion through contact with the berth or ship, should be precluded.

4.5.5   Before commencement of operations, the responsible persons on the berth and on the oil tanker should ensure:

.1   proper mooring of the oil tanker;

.2   joint completion of appropriate pre-transfer checklist(s) such as the *Ship/Shore Safety Checklist* contained in the latest edition of the *International safety guide for oil tankers and terminals* (see the appendix);

.3   availability of safe and convenient access to the oil tanker;

.4   sufficient tanker and berth personnel for safe performance of operation;

.5   availability of reliable communication with control centre and the oil tanker;

.6   availability of reliable communication between the shore facility pump room and the oil tanker;

.7   proper connection and securing of loading arms or hoses to the oil tanker's manifold;

.8   proper condition and position of loading arms or hoses, hose saddles and supports;

.9   flange joints, where used, are fully bolted and sealed;

.10   proper blanking of unused cargo and bunker connections;

.11   any valve through which oil could be discharged to the sea is closed and inspected and, if not used in the operation, is sealed to ensure that it is not inadvertently opened;

.12   deck scuppers on the oil tanker are properly plugged;

.13   availability of empty drip trays on the oil tanker under couplings of hoses, and means for drip tray drainage;

.14 availability of materials on the oil tanker for on-deck clean-up in case of spillage;

.15 proper illumination of working places and equipment involved in the operation;

.16 a deck watch is established on the oil tanker to pay particular attention to moorings, hoses and manifold integrity;

.17 correct understanding of commands and signals by the responsible person on the oil tanker during operations and in emergency situations; and

.18 security protocols are agreed.

4.5.6   The operation may be started only after the responsible person on the oil tanker and the responsible person on the berth have agreed to do so, either verbally or in writing.

4.6   Performance of operations

4.6.1   The operation should be started at a slow rate in order to ensure that all connections, loading arms or hoses are tight, that the oil is being directed into intended pipelines and tanks, that no excessive pressure is being built up in the hoses and pipelines, and that there is no evidence of oil leakage in way of the tanker's hull.

4.6.2   Only after being satisfied that there is no leakage, that the oil is being transferred into the intended pipelines and tanks, and that there is no excessive pressure, may the rate of transfer be increased up to the maximum indicated in the plan of operation.

4.6.3   The responsible persons on the berth and on board the oil tanker should have in place an effective means of monitoring the following (and, if necessary, ensure the appropriate remedial action is taken):

.1 for any leakage from the equipment and system, or through the oil tanker's plating;

.2 that there is no leakage into pump rooms, ballast or void spaces or cargo tanks that are not scheduled to be loaded;

.3 if there is any excessive pressure in piping and hoses;

.4 the mooring arrangements;

.5 the condition of loading arms and hoses and their support arrangements; and

.6 tank ullages and quantities transferred.

4.6.4   Care must be taken to prevent surge pressures during loading when changing over tanks on the oil tanker. The filling valves of the next tanks in sequence should be opened before the valves on the tank being filled are closed.

4.6.5   Information on quantities transferred should be routinely and regularly exchanged between the oil tanker and the facility control centre. Any significant discrepancies between the quantity discharged and the quantity received should be promptly investigated.

4.6.6   The responsible persons on the berth and on the oil tanker should collaborate regarding necessary changes in mooring arrangements.

4.7   Completion of operations

4.7.1   During oil tanker loading operations, it should be ensured that adequate ullage space is left in each tank being filled. When it is required to stop cargo transfer operations, the responsible person should advise the pumping station in ample time. When non-return valves are not fitted in the shore system, all necessary precautions should be taken to prevent oil flowing back into the tanker.

4.7.2   On crude oil tankers, all main cargo lines should be drained and pumped ashore through the small diameter "MARPOL pipeline" provided for that purpose (see paragraph 3.2.3.8).

4.7.3   Before loading arms or hoses are disconnected, they should be drained as far as is practical and any residual product should be contained in the manifold drip tray. Following disconnection, the loading arm or hose should be securely sealed or blanked.

4.7.4   As soon as practicable after the transfer operation has been completed, and before unmooring, the responsible persons should ensure that all valves in the systems are closed and cargo tank openings are closed and secured for sea.

4.8   Suspension of operations

4.8.1   Operations should be suspended when:

.1   wind and sea conditions exceed the permissible limits for safe operation at the berth;

.2   movement of the oil tanker alongside or to seaward reaches the maximum permissible and may risk damaging loading arms or hoses;

.3   there is a failure of the main communication system between the berth and the control centre or berth and the oil tanker, and there are no proper standby communications;

.4   there is a power failure in the facility or on the oil tanker;

.5   any escape of oil into the sea is discovered;

.6   there is an unexplained pressure drop in the cargo system;

.7   fire danger is discovered;

.8   any oil leakage is discovered from hoses, couplings, loading arms, pipelines of the facility or the oil tanker's deck piping;

.9   overflow of oil onto the deck occurs caused by overfilling of a cargo tank;

.10   any faults or damage threatening the escape of oil are discovered;

.11   there is a failure of illumination or poor visibility at the berth; and

.12   there is a significant, unexplained difference between the quantities of cargo delivered and received.

4.8.2   Operations may be resumed only after the weather and seas have abated or appropriate remedial action has been taken.

4.9   Cautionary notices

4.9.1   Cautionary notices, containing information on local regulations relating to oil pollution, should be installed on the berth and oil tanker in readily visible places.

4.10   Documents

4.10.1   A set of documents should always be kept at each berth at a place easily accessible for the personnel, each set including:

.1   an operating manual containing procedures, practices and drawings relevant to the specific facility;

.2 terminal information and port regulations;

.3 a security plan;

.4 a contingency plan for dealing with accidental oil spillages;

.5 emergency procedures and instructions for the berth personnel;

.6 a manual on prevention of pollution of the marine environment; and

.7 a berth operations log book.

4.10.2 The facility should maintain a set of up-to-date documents to ensure compliance with regulations, procedures and good practice. Documentation should provide current information on topics that include:

.1 legislation, including national and local requirements;

.2 industry guidance and company policies;

.3 operating manuals, maintenance and inspection procedures, site plans and drawings;

.4 records, for example, of audits, inspections, meetings, permits and local procedures;

.5 certificates issued for equipment and processes; and

.6 a record of violations and details of remedial action taken.

4.11 Training

4.11.1 Owners or operators of berths are responsible for ensuring that personnel engaged in activities relating to oil transfer operations are trained and competent in their duties. The training should include the following:

.1 the proper operation and maintenance of equipment at the facility;

.2 measures for the prevention of oil pollution;

.3 role in pollution response;

.4 role in fire fighting;

.5 dealing with other emergencies and security incidents; and

.6 international, national, local and company requirements for safe and pollution free operations.

4.11.2   Owners or operators of berths should plan, schedule and conduct exercises to develop a sound knowledge of application of the oil spill contingency plan. Such exercises and instruction should include familiarization of the personnel with safety measures, typical faults of systems and equipment, and latest techniques for combating spillages.

4.11.3   It should be ensured that berth personnel are familiar with the contents of the facility's *Operations Manual* as it relates to the operation of the berth, its systems and equipment. Particular attention should be paid to instructing the shore personnel concerning the communication systems and means of effective communication with oil tanker personnel.

4.11.4   Appropriate training records for individual personnel should be maintained at the facility.

4.12   Oil spill response

4.12.1   Arrangements must be in place to train staff and provide equipment so that any spillage can be contained and dealt with in a timely manner. Oil, particularly crude oil, spreads over the surface of the water very rapidly so remedial operations should be started as soon as possible after a spill has been reported, preferably within minutes of the report. The immediate actions must be focused on stopping the outflow and containing and cleaning up the oil before it spreads.

4.12.2   During transfer operations at a berth, there should always be a trained group available that is prepared to take immediate action should a spill occur. This trained group may be supplemented by others drawn from their normal duties to assist in combating the effects of an oil spill. The necessary equipment and materials should be available at all times. Constant vigilance and the immediate availability of trained resources and equipment are essential for effective oil spill response.

4.12.3   Facilities should periodically carry out spill response drills, which should include notifications, tabletop exercises and equipment deployment. Facility personnel should participate in local, regional and national spill drills to test equipment and ensure the capability of personnel.

For further information on oil spill response, reference should be made to the *Manual on Oil Pollution, Section IV – Combating Oil Spills*.

4.13 Prevention, clean-up and reporting

4.13.1 For each berth or group of berths there should be a contingency plan in the event of accidental oil spillage during the course of operations. This contingency plan should be integrated, as appropriate, with other contingency plans applicable to the entire port area.

4.13.2 The contingency plan should be approved by the appropriate authority and should list key personnel with their locations and emergency telephone numbers. It should also contain details about the location of essential equipment and materials, and who should be contacted to obtain them.

4.13.3 The oil transfer operation should be stopped if any spill occurs and the immediate measures set forth in the contingency plan should be implemented. The appropriate authorities should be informed of any oil spillage, its size, nature and cause, and each case and/or oil spillage must be recorded in the oil tanker's *Oil Record Book* and the facility's *Oil Operations Log*.

4.13.4 In the event of spillage of 100 tonnes and above, a report is to be prepared in the form recommended by IMO. It should be forwarded to the Administration of the coastal State, or to the flag State Administration if the vessel is in waters beyond the jurisdiction of the coastal State. In either case, the forms should then be forwarded to IMO in accordance with the IMO's *Guidelines for reporting incidents involving dangerous goods, harmful substances and/or marine pollutants*.

4.14 References

Manual on Oil Pollution Section II – Contingency Planning – (IMO)

Manual on Oil Pollution Section IV – Combating Oil Spills – (IMO)

International Safety Guide for Oil Tankers and Terminals (ISGOTT) – (IAPH/ICS/OCIMF)

Mooring equipment guidelines – (OCIMF)

Recommendations for oil tanker manifolds and associated equipment – (OCIMF)

Marine terminal baseline criteria and assessment questionnaire – (OCIMF)

Chapter 5
Oil tanker operations at offshore berths
(single point and buoy moorings)

5.1 General

5.1.1 The loading or discharging of an oil tanker at a single point or buoy mooring berth is conducted by connecting floating or submerged hoses or fixed arms between the cargo manifold on board the oil tanker in such a way as to permit the transfer of oil without leakage. The oil tanker manifold may be situated at the bow, the stern or either side amidships. The operation should always be controlled so as to prevent any escape or spillage of oil.

Figure 4 – *Single point mooring (Source OCIMF)*

5.1.2 All normal pollution prevention measures taken while alongside a jetty are applicable when an oil tanker is at a buoy mooring. A buoy mooring, whether single or multi-buoy, should be capable of accommodating the largest oil tanker likely to use it in all sea and weather conditions (which can be reasonably expected), allowing the tanker to remain safely afloat and to proceed at all times with sufficient under-keel clearance. During the time the tanker is at buoy mooring, frequent and regular inspection of mooring lines and cargo hoses is essential. Excessive movement of the oil tanker may cause rupture of the ship's connections to the buoy. Cargo hoses must not be subjected to mooring forces. Additionally, when at a single buoy mooring, frequent inspections should be made from the bow to ensure that the oil tanker does not make contact with the buoy.

5.1.3   The following basic principles should be applied if pollution is to be avoided:

.1   all personnel concerned with the loading or discharge of oil should be fully aware of the need to prevent pollution;

.2   all personnel should adhere strictly to the joint plan of operations including the provision of an efficient communication system;

.3   the responsible persons should check the items listed in paragraph 5.5.3 before the oil actually flows;

.4   all personnel involved should be aware of the immediate measures and response necessary in the event of an escape of oil; and

.5   all equipment, the failure of which might result in an escape of oil, should be inspected and tested regularly.

5.2   General description of facilities and their mooring arrangements

5.2.1   Single point mooring (SPM)

5.2.1.1   A single point mooring (SPM) is an integrated mooring arrangement for bow mooring a conventional tanker. Examples include bow mooring arrangements to a catenary anchor leg mooring (CALM) system, to a single anchor leg mooring system (SALM) or to a FPSO or FSU. Transfer of oil is generally through a floating hose from the SPM to the oil tanker's manifold. Operations at FPSOs and FSUs are addressed in chapter 7 of this manual.

Figure 5 – *Single point mooring (Source OCIMF)*

5.2.1.2 Fundamental to the safety and integrity of operations at a SPM is the provision of compatible equipment by the terminal and the ship to ensure safe mooring arrangements are in place. These arrangements are detailed in the industry guidance *Recommendations for equipment employed in the bow mooring of conventional tankers at single point moorings* (OCIMF) and include the provision of the following:

> **.1** terminal operators should provide one or two mooring hawsers, each of which terminates at the shipboard end with a chafe chain approximately 8 metres or more in length composed of 76 mm stud link chain. A pick-up rope should be connected to the chafe chain and should typically consist of 150 metres of 80 mm diameter synthetic fibre rope having a minimum breaking load of 75 tonnes;

.2 oil tankers trading to SPMs should be equipped with one or two bow chain stoppers designed to accept 76 mm chain and having a minimum safe working load (SWL) of between 200 and 350 tonnes, depending on the vessel's size and age, as detailed in the industry guidance referenced above. The bow chain stopper(s) should be located between 2.7 and 3.7 metres inboard of the bow fairlead(s);

.3 bow fairlead(s), having a SWL that is at least equivalent to the bow chain stopper(s) that they serve, should measure at least 600 x 450 mm. If two bow chain stoppers are fitted, the distance apart of the two bow fairleads should, if practical, be at least 2 metres (centre to centre) but in no case more than 3.0 metres;

.4 arrangements should be in place to safely handle pick-up ropes, ideally by providing a direct straight lead through the bow fairlead and bow chain stopper to a winch storage drum. Where it is not possible to provide a direct lead, the use of pedestal rollers may be required, the number and position of which should be as detailed in the industry guidance; and

.5 winch storage drums used to stow the pick-up rope should be capable of lifting at least 15 tonnes and be of sufficient size to accommodate 150 metres of 80 mm diameter rope. The use of winch drum ends (warping ends) to handle pick-up ropes is considered unsafe and should be avoided.

5.2.2 Multi buoy moorings (MBMs)

5.2.2.1 Two main configurations of multi buoy moorings are commonly used, as follows:

.1 Conventional buoy moorings (CBMs) are offshore marine berths in which the oil tanker's bow is held in position by its own anchors and three to seven mooring buoys are installed to secure the stern, as shown in figure 6. CBMs are the most common type of MBM installed worldwide. This design is the preferred option for a MBM as it provides the least amount of obstructions during berthing and unberthing, and is the most cost-effective in terms of fabrication and installation. The disadvantage of a CBM is that it relies on the oil tanker's anchors to provide the bow restraint. The anchors provide limited mooring capacity compared to permanent mooring legs, thus this type of arrangement may be limited to smaller ship sizes or sites with relatively mild environmental conditions; and

.2   All buoy moorings (ABMs) are offshore marine berths in which both the oil tanker's bow and stern are held in position by mooring. ABMs are generally located where bottom conditions prevent the use of the oil tanker's anchors or where additional mooring restraint is needed for the maximum expected environmental conditions. The anchors may be used for manoeuvring but are not considered part of the required mooring restraint.

5.2.2.2 Mooring legs for both CBMs and ABMs consist of anchoring point(s), chain ground leg(s), bridle (if required), chain in thrash zone, a pendant section incorporating a swivel, and a mooring buoy to which the ship's mooring line can be attached.

5.2.2.3 For either a CBM or ABM arrangement, the cargo transfer system consists of one or more subsea pipelines that run between the shoreline and the MBM. Oil tanker loading and unloading operations are carried out using flexible hose strings that are connected between the offshore end of the subsea pipelines, the pipeline end manifold (PLEM), and the oil tanker's manifold.

Figure 6 – *Multi buoy mooring (Source OCIMF)*

5.3 Hoses

5.3.1   Hoses used for the transfer of oil at single point and multi buoy moorings should be manufactured and tested in accordance with a recognized international standard or an accepted industry code, such as that detailed in the OCIMF publication *Guide to manufacturing and purchasing hoses for offshore moorings*.

5.3.2   The material and design of the hoses should be compatible with the cargo to be transferred and be suited for the maximum pressure range and flow rates anticipated to be encountered in service.

5.3.3   The length of the hose string(s) should be suitable to permit safe handling of the largest oil tanker acceptable at the terminal. Sufficient length should be provided to prevent excessive strain being placed on the hoses in normal service and to ensure that the hose is not subjected to bends smaller than its minimum bend radius.

5.3.4   The maximum weight of the hose to be lifted for connection to the oil tanker's manifold should be calculated by the facility. It should be noted that hose movement in wave conditions may impose additional dynamic loads and it is recommended that an allowance of 1.5 x static weight is used if it is likely that significant waves greater than 1 metre will be experienced at the facility.

Figure 7 – *Hose fitting in preparation for transfer operation (Source OCIMF)*

5.3.5   It should be ensured that the SWL of the oil tanker's lifting equipment is sufficient to enable safe handling of the hose. The SWLs of lifting equipment on oil tankers above 16,000 dwt are described in the OCIMF publication *Recommendations for oil tanker manifolds and associated equipment.*

5.3.6   Arrangements at the oil tanker's manifold should be such as to prevent excessive bending of the hose. In order to protect the hose from sharp edges and obstructions, a horizontal curved plate or rounded pipe section should be fitted at the ship's side to provide hose support.

5.3.7   Hoses should be properly suspended and supported throughout the transfer operation by the use of lifting bridles and saddles. Measures should be taken to ensure that excessive loads are not placed on the oil tanker's manifolds.

5.3.8   Floating hoses should be inspected ashore at regular intervals and tested to the appropriate standards as established by the hose manufacturer. Submerged hoses should be regularly inspected by divers. They may also be hydrostatically tested in place, or may be removed for inspection and testing onshore to the appropriate standards, as established by the manufacturer.

5.3.9   Floating or submerged hose assemblies should be cleared of oil before they are disconnected for testing or survey and due care should be taken to avoid any spillage of oil. All open ends on the hose assembly and on fixed installations should be blanked immediately after disconnection.

5.3.10   Hoses should be withdrawn from service and retired against defined criteria, which may include the following:

.1   the presence of defects detected during visual inspections. Defects prompting retirement could include irregularities in the outside diameter, such as kinking, damaged or exposed reinforcement or permanent deformation of the casing and damage, slippage or misalignment of end fittings;

.2   after a defined period in service, established in consultation with the manufacturer; and

.3   when the temporary elongation of the hose, measured during routine pressure tests, exceeds maximum allowable values.

5.3.11   Test data with respect to each hose should be available at the facility.

5.3.12   Each hose should bear the following durable indelible markings:

.1   the manufacturer's name or trademark;

.2   identification of the standard specification for manufacture;

.3   factory test pressure (note: equal to rated working pressure, maximum working pressure, maximum allowable working pressure);

.4   month and year of manufacture and manufacturer's serial number;

.5   indication that the hose is electrically continuous or electrically discontinuous, semi-continuous or anti-static; and

.6   the type of service for which it is intended, e.g. oil or chemical.

5.3.13   A visual inspection of the hose and ancillary fittings should be carried out before the hose is connected to the oil tanker's manifold to determine that there is no damage. If damage to a hose, flange or fittings is present, the hose or fitting should be withdrawn from use for further inspection, repair or retirement.

5.3.14   Depending on their design, the elements of each hose assembly should meet the following requirements:

.1   threaded couplings should ensure the security of connection without any additional fixing arrangements;

.2   flanged joints should meet the requirements of international standards for connecting sizes, and their material and design should correspond to accepted standards; and

.3   quick release couplings should meet the requirements of international standards for connecting sizes. Their material and design should correspond to accepted standards.

5.4   Control and communications

5.4.1   Each single point or buoy mooring berth should have a centre from which the operation is controlled.

5.4.2   The operation centre should be equipped with radio or telephone, ensuring reliable two-way communications by voice between the responsible person in the centre and the responsible person on the oil tanker. The communications shall be in an agreed language understood by both persons.

5.4.3   Means shall be provided for control of the operations and for emergency stopping of the flow.

5.5   Preparation for operations

5.5.1   The Master of an oil tanker should be fully advised of the availability of tugs and mooring craft, and of any particular features of the berth. He should also be advised on any local regulations regarding pollution.

5.5.2   A joint plan of operation should be developed on the basis of information exchanged between the oil tanker and the control centre, comprising the following:

.1   mooring arrangements;

.2   quantities and characteristics of the cargo(es) to be loaded (discharged) and identification of any toxic components;

.3   sequence of loading (discharging) of tanks;

.4   details of cargo transfer system, number of pumps and maximum permissible pressure;

.5   rate of oil transfer during operations (initial, maximum and topping-up);

.6   the time required for starting, stopping and changing rate of delivery during topping-off of tanks;

.7   normal stopping and emergency shutdown procedures;

.8   disposition and quantity of ballast and slops, and disposal if applicable;

.9   maximum draught and freeboard anticipated during operation;

.10   details of proposed method of venting or inerting cargo tanks;

.11   details of crude oil washing, if applicable;

.12   emergency and oil spill containment procedures;

.13   sequence of actions in case of spillage of oil;

.14   specific conditions of operations (if any);

.15   environmental and operational limits that would trigger suspension of the transfer operation, disconnection of hoses and removal of the oil tanker from the mooring;

.16 local or government rules that apply to the transfer; and

.17 co-ordination of plans for cargo hose connection, monitoring, draining and disconnection.

5.5.3 Before commencement of operations the responsible persons should ensure:

.1 proper mooring of the oil tanker;

.2 availability of reliable communication with control centre and tanker;

.3 joint completion of appropriate pre-transfer checklist(s);

.4 proper connection and securing of hoses to the oil tanker's manifold;

.5 proper condition and position of hoses, hose saddles and supports;

.6 flange joints, where used, are fully bolted and sealed;

.7 proper blanking of unused cargo and bunker connections;

.8 any valve through which oil could be discharged to the sea is closed and inspected and, if not used in the operation, is sealed to ensure that it is not inadvertently opened;

.9 deck scuppers are properly plugged;

.10 availability of empty drip trays on the oil tanker under couplings of hoses, and means for drip tray drainage;

.11 availability of materials on the oil tanker for on-deck clean-up in case of spillage;

.12 proper illumination of working places and equipment involved in the operation;

.13 a deck watch is established to pay particular attention to moorings, hoses and manifold integrity;

.14 correct understanding of commands and signals by the responsible person on the oil tanker during operations and in emergency situations; and

.15 unmooring plan.

5.5.4   The operation may be started only after the responsible person on the oil tanker and the responsible person in the control centre have agreed to do so, either verbally or in writing.

5.6   Performance of operations

5.6.1   The operation should be started at a slow rate in order to ensure that all connections and hoses are tight, that the oil is being directed into intended pipelines and tanks, that no excessive pressure is being built up in the hoses and pipelines, and that there is no evidence of oil leakage in way of the tanker's hull.

5.6.2   The rate of transfer may be increased to the maximum indicated in the plan of operation, however this can only be done when it is certain that there is no leakage, the oil is being transferred into the intended pipelines and tanks, and there is no excessive pressure.

5.6.3   The responsible person on board the oil tanker should periodically check the following and, if necessary, take appropriate remedial action:

.1   for any leakage from the equipment and system, or through the oil tanker's plating;

.2   that there is no leakage into pump rooms, ballast or void spaces or cargo tanks not scheduled to be loaded;

.3   if there is any excessive pressure in piping and hoses;

.4   the mooring arrangements;

.5   the condition of hoses and their support arrangements; and

.6   tank ullages and quantities transferred.

5.6.4   Care must be taken to prevent surge pressures during loading when changing over tanks on the oil tanker. The filling valves of the next tanks in sequence should be opened before the valves on the tank being filled are closed.

5.6.5   Information on quantities transferred should be routinely and regularly exchanged between the ship and shore control centre. Any significant discrepancies between the quantity discharged and the quantity received should be promptly investigated.

5.6.6   At SPMs, constant attention should be paid to the relative position of the oil tanker and the SPM in order that early action may be taken to prevent the oil tanker riding up to and contacting the mooring. Remedial action, if required, may include the use of the main engine astern or the employment of a tug to push back the vessel.

5.7   Completion of operations

5.7.1   During oil tanker loading operations, it should be ensured that adequate ullage space is left in each tank being filled. When it is required to stop cargo transfer operations, the responsible person should advise the pumping station in ample time. When non return valves are not fitted in the shore system, all necessary precautions should be taken to prevent oil flowing back into the tanker.

5.7.2   Before hoses are disconnected, they should be drained as far as is practical and any residual product should be contained in the manifold drip tray. The hose should be securely blanked prior to being released in a controlled manner and lowered to the water in accordance with terminal procedures.

5.7.3   As soon as practicable after the transfer operation has been completed, and before unmooring, the responsible person should ensure that all valves in the system are closed and cargo tank openings are closed and secured for sea.

5.7.4   Unmooring should be in accordance with the plan, with lines released in the agreed sequence.

5.8   Suspension of operations

5.8.1   Operations should be suspended when:

.1   wind and sea conditions exceed the permissible limits for safe operation at the mooring;

.2   there is a power failure on the oil tanker;

.3   there is a failure of the main communication system between the control centre and the oil tanker and there are no proper standby communications;

.4   any escape of oil into the sea is discovered;

.5   there is an unexplained pressure drop in the cargo system;

.6   fire danger is discovered;

.7   any oil leakage is discovered from hoses, couplings, or the oil tanker's deck piping;

.8   overflow of oil onto the deck occurs caused by overfilling of a cargo tank;

.9   any faults or damage threatening the escape of oil are discovered; and

.10   there is a significant, unexplained difference between the quantities of cargo delivered and received.

5.8.2   Operations may be resumed only after the weather and seas have abated or appropriate remedial action has been taken.

5.9   Training

5.9.1   Owners or operators of single point or buoy mooring berths bear the responsibility for the proper instruction of personnel on current legislation, the operation and maintenance of equipment, measures for the prevention of oil pollution, and methods for dealing with spillages.

5.9.2   Owners or operators of single point or buoy mooring berths should plan, schedule and conduct exercises to develop a sound knowledge of application of the contingency plan. Such exercises and instructions should include familiarization of the personnel with safety measures, typical faults of systems and equipment, and the latest techniques of combating spillages.

5.10   Oil spill response

5.10.1   This subject is adequately covered in paragraph 4.12 of this manual and Section IV of the *Manual on Oil Pollution: Combating Oil Spills*, which deals with practical information on means of dealing with oil spillages. In addition, for single point or buoy moorings, it would be desirable to have a tender or work vessel available at all times to deploy response equipment and to conduct clean-up of any oil, which might be spilled during the transfer operation.

5.11   Prevention, clean-up and reporting

5.11.1   This subject is covered in paragraph 4.13 of this manual.

5.12   References

International safety guide for oil tankers and terminals (ISGOTT) – (IAPH/ICS/OCIMF)

Recommendations for equipment employed in the bow mooring of conventional tankers at single point moorings – (OCIMF)

Mooring equipment guidelines – (OCIMF)

Guide to manufacturing and purchasing hoses for offshore moorings – (OCIMF)

Guidelines for the handling, storage, inspection and testing of hoses in the field – (OCIMF)

Recommendations for oil tanker manifolds and associated equipment – (OCIMF)

Chapter 6
Ship-to-ship transfer of crude oil and petroleum products while underway or at anchor

6.1 Introduction

6.1.1 This chapter of the manual includes general provisions, which may be supplemented by special instruction from the shipowners on how to implement procedures based on the peculiarities of design, oil tanker equipment and operational conditions. Ship-to-ship transfer operations can be performed efficiently, smoothly and without danger if the Master and the crew are sufficiently experienced and trained. This chapter of the manual is intended for Masters and crews directly involved in ship-to-ship oil transfer operations. A typical operation is shown in figure 8. For further information, please refer to *Ship-to-ship transfer guide – petroleum*.

6.1.2 The contents of this chapter shall not apply to oil transfer operations associated with fixed or floating platforms including drilling rigs; floating production, storage and offloading facilities (FPSOs) used for the offshore production and storage of oil; and floating storage units (FSUs) used for the offshore storage of produced oil.

6.1.3 In addition, the reporting requirements contained in this chapter may not necessarily apply to bunkering operations. It is recommended that owners, chartered Masters and ships' agents obtain advice from the necessary local authorities.

6.1.4 The guidance contained in this chapter shall not apply to STS operations necessary for the purpose of securing the safety of a ship or saving life at sea, or for combating specific pollution incidents in order to minimize the damage from pollution, but does represent good practice.

6.1.5 The contents of this chapter shall not apply to STS operations where either of the ships involved is a warship, naval auxiliary or other ship owned or operated by a State and used, for the time being, only on government non commercial service. However, each State shall ensure, by the adoption of appropriate measures not impairing operations or operational capabilities of such ships that the STS operations are conducted in a manner consistent, so far as is reasonable and practicable, with this chapter.

Figure 8 – *Preparing for ship-to-ship transfer (Source OCIMF)*

6.2 General requirements for vessels involved in ship-to-ship transfer operations

6.2.1 Person in overall advisory control

6.2.1.1 A ship-to-ship transfer operation should be under the advisory control of a designated mooring/unmooring Master, who will either be one of the Masters concerned or an STS Superintendent. It is not intended that the person in overall advisory control in any way relieves the ships' Masters of any of their duties, requirements or responsibilities.

6.2.1.2 The person in overall advisory control of STS operations shall be qualified to perform all relevant duties, taking into account the qualifications contained in the best practice guidelines for STS operations identified by the Organization (IMO's *Manual on Oil Pollution, Section I, Prevention* as amended, and the ICS and OCIMF publication *Ship-to-ship transfer guide – petroleum*, fourth edition, 2005). The Administration, cargo owners or oil tanker's operators should agree and designate the person in overall advisory control who should have at least the following qualifications:

> .1 an appropriate management level deck licence or certificate meeting international certification standards, with all International Convention on Standards of Training, Certification and

Watchkeeping for Seafarers 1978, (STCW Convention) and dangerous cargo endorsements up to date and appropriate for the ships engaged in the STS operation;

.2   attendance at a suitable ship handling course;

.3   conduct of a suitable number of mooring/unmooring operations in similar circumstances and with similar vessels;

.4   experience in oil tanker cargo loading and unloading;

.5   a thorough knowledge of the geographic transfer area and surrounding areas;

.6   a knowledge of spill clean-up techniques, including familiarity with the equipment and resources available in the STS contingency plan; and

.7   a thorough knowledge of the STS operations plan.

6.2.1.3   The person in overall advisory control should:

.1   ensure that the cargo transfer, mooring and unmooring operations are conducted in accordance with the required STS operations plan, the contents of this chapter of the manual, and take into account the recommendations contained in the industry publication *Ship-to-ship transfer guide – petroleum*;

.2   advise the Master(s) of the critical phases of the cargo transfer, mooring and unmooring operation;

.3   ensure the provisions of the contingency plan are carried out in the event of a spill;

.4   ensure that all required reports are made to the appropriate authorities;

.5   ensure that crew members involved in each aspect of the operation are properly briefed and understand their responsibilities;

.6   before any approach and mooring operations are attempted, ensure that proper and effective communication has been confirmed between the two oil tankers and appropriate checks have been completed;

.7   ensure that a pre-transfer STS safety check is undertaken in accordance with accepted industry guidance; and

.8   ensure that appropriate checks are undertaken prior to unmooring.

6.2.1.4 The person in overall advisory control should have the authority to advise:

.1   suspend or terminate the STS operation; and

.2   review the STS operations plan for that particular operation.

6.2.1.5 Each oil tanker should have a person in charge of the cargo transfer operation on board, during each watch, throughout the operation. Each person in charge shall:

.1   inspect the cargo transfer system before transfer;

.2   supervise all aspects of the transfer operation on board the oil tanker;

.3   conduct the transfer operation in accordance with the STS operations plan; and

.4   ensure that all moorings, fenders and safety measures are checked.

6.2.2   STS transfer area

6.2.2.1 The STS transfer area should be specially selected for safe operations, in co-ordination with the appropriate authorities. In selecting the area for STS transfer, the following should be taken into account, in particular in the absence of any applicable national legislation:

.1   the traffic density in the given area;

.2   the need for sufficient sea room and water depth required for manoeuvring during mooring and unmooring;

.3   the availability of safe anchorage with good holding ground;

.4   present and forecasted weather conditions;

.5   availability of weather reports for the areas;

.6   distance from shore logistical support;

.7   proximity to environmentally sensitive areas; and

.8   security threat.

6.2.3 Notification to authorities

6.2.3.1 Each oil tanker subject to regulation 42 of chapter 8, MARPOL Annex I, as amended by resolution MEPC.186(59), that plans STS operations within the territorial sea, or the exclusive economic zone of a Party to the present Convention shall notify that Party not less than 48 hours in advance of the scheduled STS operations.

Where, in an exceptional case, STS operations are to take place within 48 hours' notice, the oil tanker shall notify the Party to the present Convention at the earliest opportunity.

The notification specified in paragraph 1 of regulation 42 shall include at least the following:

.1 name, flag, call sign, IMO number and estimated time of arrival of the oil tankers involved in the STS operations;

.2 date, time and geographical location at the commencement of the planned STS operations;

.3 whether STS operations are to be conducted at anchor or underway;

.4 oil type and quantity;

.5 planned duration of the STS operations;

.6 identification of STS operations service provider or person in overall advisory control and contact information; and

.7 confirmation that the oil tanker has on board an STS operations plan.

If the estimated time of arrival of an oil tanker at the location or area for the STS operations changes by more than six hours, the master, owner or agent of that oil tanker shall provide a revised estimated time of arrival to the applicable national maritime authority.

6.2.3.2 When STS transfers are to be conducted in an area in international waters, a vessel(s) should transmit by radio a navigational warning (security) to all ships stating:

.1 the name and nationality of the vessels involved in the operation;

.2 the geographical position of operations and general headings;

.3 nature of operations;

.4   the planned start time of the operations and expected duration; and

.5   request for wide berth and the need to exercise caution when navigating in the STS transfer area.

6.2.3.3 On completion of the STS operation, the person having overall advisory control or his designee should cancel the navigational warning.

6.2.4   STS operations plan

6.2.4.1 Each oil tanker involved in the cargo transfer operation should have on board a plan approved by the relevant national maritime Administration prescribing how to conduct STS operations. The STS operations plan must be written in the working language understood by the ship's officers.

The STS operations plan shall be developed taking into account the information contained in the best practice guidelines for STS operations identified by the Organization. The STS operations plan may be incorporated into an existing Safety Management System required by chapter IX of the *International Convention for the Safety of Life at Sea (SOLAS), 1974,* as amended, if that requirement is applicable to the oil tanker in question. Any oil tanker subject to this chapter and engaged in STS operations shall comply with its STS operations plan.

6.2.4.2 A copy of the STS operations plan should be available at the following locations on each oil tanker:

.1   the bridge;

.2   the cargo transfer control station; and

.3   the engine room.

6.2.4.3 The STS operations plan should contain the following information:

.1   a step-by-step description of the entire STS operation;

.2   a description of the mooring and unmooring procedures and arrangements, including diagrams where necessary, and procedures for tending the oil tanker's moorings during the transfer of cargo;

.3   a description of the cargo and ballast transfer procedures, including those used while the ship is either underway or anchored, as well as procedures for:

      .1   connecting and testing the integrity of cargo hoses and the hose to manifold interface;

      .2   topping off cargo tanks; and

      .3   disconnecting cargo hoses.

.4   the titles, locations and duties of all persons involved in the STS operation;

.5   procedures for operating the emergency shutdown and communication systems, and for rapid breakaway;

.6   a description of the drip trays and procedures for emptying them;

.7   procedures for reporting spillages of oil into the water;

.8   an approved contingency plan, which meets the requirements of paragraph 6.2.9; and

.9   a cargo and ballast plan.

6.2.4.4 The Master of each oil tanker should ensure that the STS operations plan on board is current and that all personnel on board follow the procedures in the Plan. Records of STS operations shall be retained on board for three years and be readily available for inspection.

6.2.5   Communications

6.2.5.1 Good, reliable communications between the two oil tankers is an essential requirement for the safe and successful conduct of STS transfer operations. In order to prevent misunderstanding and possibly incorrect interpretations of commands and signals, communications between the oil tankers should be conducted in a common language mutually agreed upon and known to personnel directly involved in transfer operations.

Figure 9 – *Ship-to-ship transfer operation (Source OCIMF)*

6.2.5.2 The oil tankers should establish initial communications as early as practicable to plan operations and to confirm the transfer area. During this initial communication, the person in overall advisory control must be confirmed. Details of the operation, including approach, mooring, cargo transfer and unmooring plans should be discussed and agreed, together with the joint use of operational safety checklists. (See examples contained in the ICS/OCIMF *Ship-to-ship transfer guide – petroleum*, which are reproduced in the appendix).

6.2.5.3 Essential personnel on board both oil tankers involved in the operation of oil transfer should be provided with a reliable means of communication (for instance, walkie-talkies) for the duration of the operation.

6.2.5.4 In the event a significant failure of communication occurs during an approach manoeuvre, the manoeuvre should be aborted, if appropriate and safe to do so, and the subsequent actions taken by each oil tanker should be indicated by the appropriate sound signals, as prescribed in the *Convention on the International Regulations for Preventing Collisions at Sea (COLREG), 1972*.

6.2.5.5 In the event of a breakdown of communications on either oil tanker during cargo operations, the vessel should sound an agreed emergency signal. At this signal, the oil transfer operations should be suspended and only resumed after the regular means of communication have been restored.

6.2.6   Equipment

6.2.6.1   Prior to starting the ship-to-ship transfer operation, the Masters of the oil tankers should exchange information concerning the availability, readiness and compatibility of the equipment to be used in the operation.

Fenders

6.2.6.2   The oil tanker(s) should be provided with fenders (primary and secondary). These fenders should be capable of withstanding the anticipated berthing energies and should be able to distribute the forces evenly over the appropriate area of the hulls of both oil tankers. It is recommended that fenders constructed to ISO 17357 should be used. Industry best practice is that the safety valve on pneumatic fenders is inspected at intervals not exceeding two years and a certificate provided to demonstrate this.

6.2.6.3   Except in cases where the STS transfer is conducted using a dedicated lightering ship, it is probable that fendering operations will be carried out with the assistance of an STS service provider. Such companies usually have service craft available and these vessels will normally assist in positioning fenders on the relevant oil tanker.

6.2.6.4   Fenders may be secured on either oil tanker. However, landing on an unprotected hull section is less likely if the fenders are rigged on the manoeuvring ship and it is therefore preferable that fenders be secured to that ship.

6.2.6.5   The person in overall advisory control should advise the position and method of securing the fenders to the oil tankers in advance of the operation.

Hoses

6.2.6.6   The hoses used for the STS transfer of crude oils or petroleum products should be specially designed and constructed for the product being handled and the purpose for which they are being used. Hoses used should comply with EN1765 (or latest equivalent) with regard to specification for the assemblies and with BS1435 (or latest equivalent) and OCIMF guidelines with regard to their handling, inspection and testing. Hoses should bear the following durable indelible markings:

.1   the manufacturer's name or trademark;

.2   identification of the standard specification for manufacture;

> **.3** factory test pressure (note: equal to rated working pressure, maximum working pressure, maximum allowable working pressure);
>
> **.4** month and year of manufacture and manufacturer's serial number;
>
> **.5** indication that the hose is electrically continuous or electrically discontinuous, semi-continuous or anti-static; and
>
> **.6** the type of service for which it is intended, e.g. oil or chemical.

6.2.6.7 Test data with respect to each hose should be available and should be sighted prior to the hose being used for transfer.

6.2.6.8 Hoses should be withdrawn from service and retired against defined criteria, which may include the following:

> **.1** the presence of defects detected during visual inspections. Defects prompting retirement could include irregularities in the outside diameter, such as kinking, damaged or exposed reinforcement or permanent deformation of the casing and damage, slippage or misalignment of end fittings;
>
> **.2** after a defined period in service, established in consultation with the manufacturer; and
>
> **.3** when the temporary elongation of the hose, measured during routine pressure tests, exceeds maximum allowable values.

6.2.6.9 A visual inspection of each of the hose assemblies should be carried out before they are connected to the manifolds to determine that they are free of damage. If damage to a hose or flange is present, the hose should be withdrawn from use for further inspection, repair or retirement.

6.2.6.10 STS transfer operations require hose connections to be well made. Flanges or, if used, quick release couplings should be in good condition and properly secured to ensure leak tight connections. Prior to transfer operations, hose integrity should be confirmed at the manifold interfaces and any intermediate flanges.

Mooring equipment

6.2.6.11 To ensure the security of moorings, it is important that both oil tankers are fitted with good quality mooring lines, efficient winches and sufficiently strong closed fairleads, bitts and other associated mooring equipment that is fit for purpose. Effective leads between fairleads and mooring bitts and mooring winches should be available for the handling of all mooring lines.

6.2.6.12 All fairleads used should be of the enclosed type, except on an oil tanker that will always have a substantially greater freeboard than the other. This will ensure that the fairleads remain effective in controlling mooring line leads as the freeboard difference between the two oil tankers changes.

6.2.6.13 A prime consideration in mooring during STS operations is to provide fairleads and bitts for all lines without the possibility of lines chaffing against each other, the oil tankers or the fenders.

6.2.6.14 Steel wire mooring lines and high modulus synthetic fibre ropes should be fitted with synthetic fibre tails to provide the additional elasticity required for STS mooring arrangements.

6.2.6.15 A minimum of four strong rope messengers should be available on both oil tankers, preferably made from a buoyant synthetic fibre material.

6.2.7 Precautions against pollution

6.2.7.1 All oil transfer operations should cease should an unsafe or environmentally hazardous condition develop. Such conditions may include:

.1 failure of hoses or moorings;

.2 deterioration of weather and/or sea conditions;

.3 a dangerous concentration of gas on the deck of the oil tanker(s); and

.4 a significant spill of oil.

6.2.8 State of readiness for an emergency

6.2.8.1 The following arrangements should be made on both oil tankers:

.1 main engine and steering gear maintained ready for immediate use;

.2 cargo pump and all other equipment trips relevant to the transfer are tested prior to the operation;

.3 crew are readily available and systems are prepared ready to drain and disconnect hoses at short notice;

.4 oil spill containment equipment is prepared and ready for use;

.5 mooring equipment is maintained ready for immediate use with extra mooring lines available at mooring stations as replacements in case of line failure; and

.6 firefighting equipment is ready for immediate use.

6.2.9 Contingency planning and emergency procedures

6.2.9.1 Although STS transfer operations can be carried out safely, the risk of accident and the potential scale of the consequences require that organizers develop contingency plans for dealing with emergencies. Before committing to an STS transfer operation, the parties involved should carry out a risk assessment covering operational hazards and the means by which they are managed. The output from the risk assessment should be used to develop risk mitigation measures and contingency plans covering all possible emergencies and providing for a comprehensive response, including the notification of relevant authorities. The contingency plan should have relevance to the location of the operation and take into account the resources available, both at the transfer location and with regard to nearby backup support.

6.2.9.2 Each oil tanker must assign emergency duties to designated members of the crew in case of accidents that may arise during the transfer of oil, particularly in the case of spillages of oil.

6.2.9.3 During each STS operation consideration should be given to having a tender or work vessel available to deploy response equipment and to conduct clean-up of any oil which may be spilled during the transfer operation.

6.2.9.4 The risk of oil pollution from STS operations is no greater than during in-port cargo transfers. However, as a transfer area may be out of range of port services, a contingency plan with the Shipboard Oil Pollution Emergency Plan (SOPEP) or Vessel Response Plan (VRP) should be available to cover such risk and should be activated in the event of an oil spill.

6.2.9.5 Any leak or spillage during the transfer should be reported immediately to the officers on cargo watch who should immediately stop the cargo transfer and notify the person in overall advisory control. The immediate measures set forth in the contingency plan should be implemented. The transfer should remain suspended until it is agreed between the relevant persons/authorities that it is safe to resume.

6.3 Risk assessment

6.3.1 STS operations should be subjected to a risk assessment, the scope of which should include confirmation of the following:

> **.1** adequate training, preparation or qualification of the oil tanker's personnel;

> **.2** suitable preparation of oil tankers for operations and sufficient control over the oil tankers during operations;

> **.3** proper understanding of signals or commands;

> **.4** adequate number of crew assigned to controlling and performing oil transfer operations;

> **.5** suitability of the agreed STS operations plan;

> **.6** adequate communications between oil tankers or responsible person(s);

> **.7** proper attention given to the differences in freeboard or the listing of the oil tankers when transferring cargo;

> **.8** the condition of transfer hoses;

> **.9** methods of securely connecting hose(s) to the oil tanker(s) manifold(s);

> **.10** recognition of the need to discontinue oil transfer when sea and weather conditions deteriorate; and

> **.11** adequacy of navigational processes.

6.4 Preparation for operations

6.4.1 Prior to the STS operation, the Masters of both oil tankers and, if appointed, the STS Superintendent, should make the following preparations before manoeuvres begin:

> **.1** carefully study the operational guidelines contained herein and in the industry publication *Ship-to-ship transfer guide – petroleum*, as well as any additional guidelines provided by the shipowner and cargo owner;

> **.2** ensure that the crew is fully briefed on procedures and hazards, with particular reference to mooring and unmoooring;

.3 ensure that the oil tanker conforms to relevant guidelines, is upright and at a suitable trim;

.4 confirm that the steering gear and all navigation and communications equipment are in satisfactory working order;

.5 confirm that engine controls have been tested and the main propulsion plant has been tested ahead and astern;

.6 confirm that all essential cargo and safety equipment has been tested;

.7 confirm that mooring equipment is prepared in accordance with the mooring plan;

.8 fenders and transfer hoses are correctly positioned, connected and secured;

.9 cargo manifolds and hose handling equipment are prepared;

.10 obtain a weather forecast for the STS transfer area for the anticipated period of the operation;

.11 agree the actions to be taken if the emergency signal on the oil tanker's whistle is sounded; and

.12 confirm completion of relevant pre-operational checklists (see examples in the appendix).

6.4.2 Communications with the master of the other oil tanker should be established in accordance with 6.2.5 at an early stage to co-ordinate the rendezvous and the method and system of approach, mooring and disengaging.

6.4.3 When the preparation of either oil tanker has been completed, the other vessel should be so informed. The operation may proceed only when both oil tankers have confirmed their readiness.

6.4.4 A joint plan of operation in alignment with the STS operations plan established for each ship should be developed on the basis of information exchanged between the two oil tankers, including the following:

.1 mooring arrangements;

.2 quantities and characteristics of the cargo(es) to be loaded (discharged) and identification of any toxic components;

.3 sequence of loading (discharging) of tanks;

.4   details of cargo transfer system, number of pumps and maximum permissible pressure;

.5   rate of oil transfer during operations (initial, maximum and topping-up);

.6   the time required by the discharging oil tanker for starting, stopping and changing rate of delivery during topping-off of tanks;

.7   normal stopping and emergency shutdown procedures;

.8   maximum draught and freeboard anticipated during operations;

.9   disposition and quantity of ballast and slops, and disposal if applicable;

.10   details of proposed method of venting or inerting cargo tanks;

.11   details of crude oil washing, if applicable;

.12   emergency and oil spill containment procedures;

.13   sequence of actions in case of spillage of oil;

.14   identified critical stages of the operation;

.15   watch or shift arrangements;

.16   environmental and operational limits that would trigger suspension of the transfer operation, and disconnection and unmooring of the tankers;

.17   local or government rules that apply to the transfer;

.18   co-ordination of plans for cargo hose connection, monitoring, draining and disconnection; and

.19   unmooring plan.

6.4.5   The cargo manifolds of the two oil tankers should be correctly aligned.

6.4.6   Hoses should be suspended in such a way that excessive strain on manifold fittings is prevented and the possibility of twisting and pinching between the oil tankers is minimized. Care should be taken to ensure that hoses are not bent to a radius less than that recommended by the manufacturer and that they do not rub against the ships' structure.

6.4.7   Before commencing the cargo transfer operation, the responsible person(s) on the oil tankers should ensure:

.1   proper mooring of the oil tanker;

.2   noting the information provided in the industry publication *Ship-to-ship transfer guide – petroleum*, as amended, availability of safe and convenient access between the oil tankers;

.3   availability of reliable communication between the two oil tankers;

.4   emergency signals and shutdown signals are agreed;

.5   proper connection and securing of hoses to the oil tanker's manifolds;

.6   proper condition and position of hoses, hose saddles and supports;

.7   flanged joints, where used, are fully bolted and sealed and ensured oil tight;

.8   proper blanking of unused cargo and bunker connections;

.9   tools required for the rapid disconnection of hoses are located at the manifold;

.10   any valve through which oil could be discharged to the sea is closed and inspected and, if not used in the operation, is sealed to ensure that it is not inadvertently opened;

.11   deck scuppers are properly plugged;

.12   availability of empty drip trays on both oil tankers under couplings of hoses, and means for drip tray drainage;

.13   availability of materials on the oil tankers for on-deck clean-up in case of spillage;

.14   fire axes or suitable cutting equipment is in position at fore and aft mooring stations;

.15   an engine room watch will be maintained throughout the transfer and the main engine will be ready for immediate use;

.16   a bridge watch and/or an anchor watch will be established;

.17   officers in charge of the cargo transfer are identified and details are posted;

> **.18** a deck watch is established to pay particular attention to moorings, fenders, hoses and manifold integrity;
>
> **.19** correct understanding of commands and signals by the responsible person(s) on the oil tankers during operations; and
>
> **.20** confirm completion of relevant pre-transfer checklists.

6.4.8 The transfer operation may be started only after the responsible person(s) on both oil tankers have agreed to do so, either verbally or in writing.

6.5 Performance of operations

6.5.1 The operation should be started at a slow rate in order to ensure that all connections and hoses are tight, the oil is being directed into intended pipelines and tanks, no excessive pressure is building up in the hoses and pipelines, and there is no evidence of oil leakage in way of the tankers' hulls.

6.5.2 Only after being satisfied that there is no leakage, the oil is being transferred into the intended pipelines and tanks, and there is no excessive pressure, may the rate of transfer be increased up to the maximum indicated in the plan of operation.

6.5.3 The responsible persons on both oil tankers should periodically check the following and, if necessary, take appropriate remedial action:

> **.1** for any leakage from the equipment and system, or through the oil tanker's plating;
>
> **.2** that there is no leakage into pump rooms, ballast or void spaces or cargo tanks not scheduled to be loaded;
>
> **.3** if there is any excessive pressure in piping and hoses;
>
> **.4** the mooring arrangements;
>
> **.5** the condition of hoses and their support arrangements; and
>
> **.6** tank ullages and quantities transferred.

6.5.4 Care must be taken to prevent surge pressures when changing over tanks on the oil tanker being loaded. The filling valves of the next tanks in sequence should be opened before the valves on the tank being filled are closed.

6.5.5   Information on quantities transferred should be routinely and regularly exchanged between the two oil tankers. Any significant discrepancies between the quantity discharged and the quantity received should be promptly investigated.

6.5.6   Cargo operations should be conducted under closed conditions with ullage, sounding and sampling ports securely closed. Due regard must be given to any local regulations that may require the adoption of vapour balancing procedures.

6.5.7   During the cargo transfer, appropriate ballast operations should be performed in order to minimize the differences in freeboard between the two oil tankers and to avoid excessive trims by the stern. Listing of either ship should be avoided, except as may be required by the discharging oil tanker to facilitate tank draining.

6.5.8   Constant attention should be paid to mooring lines and fenders to avoid chafing and undue stress, particularly that caused by changes in relative freeboard. If at any time mooring lines need to be repositioned or adjusted, this should only be done under strictly controlled conditions.

6.6   Completion of operations

6.6.1   It should be ensured that adequate ullage space is left in each tank being filled. When it is required to stop cargo transfer operations, the responsible person should advise the pumping oil tanker in ample time.

6.6.2   Upon completion of the oil transfer, the oil tanker with the greatest freeboard should close the valve at the manifold and drain the oil contained in the hoses into the tank of the other oil tanker. Any remaining oil in the hoses should be drained, after which the hoses should be disconnected and securely blanked. The cargo manifolds should also be securely blanked.

6.6.3   Following completion of any relevant checklists, the Masters should co-ordinate the unmooring plan, taking into account weather and sea conditions prevailing in the area.

6.6.4   As soon as practicable after the transfer operation has been completed, and before unmooring, the responsible person on each oil tanker should ensure that all valves in their system are closed and cargo tank openings are closed and secured for sea.

6.6.5   The oil transfer documents should be completed, communications checked and the readiness of both oil tankers established, whereupon the ships should unmoor in accordance with the plan.

6.7 Suspension of operations

6.7.1 Both oil tankers should be prepared to immediately discontinue the STS transfer operation, and to unmoor and depart if necessary. The operation should be suspended when:

.1 movement of the oil tankers alongside reaches the maximum permissible and risks placing excessive strain on hoses;

.2 under adverse weather and/or sea conditions;

.3 either oil tanker experiences a power failure;

.4 there is a failure of the main communication system between the oil tankers and there are no proper standby communications;

.5 any escape of oil into the sea is discovered;

.6 there is an unexplained pressure drop in the cargo system;

.7 fire danger is discovered;

.8 any oil leakage is discovered from hoses, couplings, or the oil tanker's deck piping;

.9 overflow of oil onto the deck occurs caused by overfilling of a cargo tank;

.10 any faults or damage threatening the escape of oil are discovered; and

.11 there is a significant, unexplained difference between the quantities of cargo delivered and received.

6.7.2 Operations may be resumed only after the weather and seas have abated or appropriate remedial action has been taken.

6.8 References

International safety guide for oil tankers and terminals (ISGOTT) – (IAPH/ICS/OCIMF)

Ship-to-ship transfer guide – petroleum – (ICS and OCIMF)

Convention on International Regulations for Preventing Collisions at Sea (COLREG), 1972 – (IMO)

Recommendations for oil tanker manifolds and associated equipment – (OCIMF)

Guidelines for the handling, storage, inspection and testing of hoses in the field – (OCIMF)

EN 1765:2004 – *Rubber hose assemblies for oil suction and discharge services – specification for the assemblies* – (European Committee for Standardization – CEN)

BS 1435-2:2005 – *Rubber hose assemblies for oil suction and discharge services – recommendations for storage, testing and use* – (British Standards Institution – BSI)

Chapter 7
Operations at offshore floating (production) storage and offloading facilities

7.1 General

7.1.1 Floating structures for production, storage and offtake have been used safely and reliably throughout the oil industry for many years. Early installations were primarily floating storage units (FSUs) but today the modern floating production, storage and offtake vessel (FPSO) includes processing equipment and a higher level of sophistication. Consequently, the FPSO is an offshore producing installation combined with a storage facility and loading terminal. The contents of this chapter shall not be governed by MARPOL Annex I, Chapter 8, which refers to the prevention of pollution during transfer of oil cargos between oil tankers at sea (STS operations).

Figure 10 – *Floating production storage and offloading unit (Source OCIMF)*

7.1.2   The scope of the operational environment for FPSOs and FSUs has broadened in recent years with units now operating in very deep water, harsh weather conditions and areas affected by sea ice. FPSOs and FSUs that are capable of disconnecting from their mooring and production riser are increasing in numbers to permit development of oil fields that are subject to weather or ice events that require the unit to move off station. Once the unit has disconnected from its mooring system, it is regarded as an "oil tanker" for the applicability of MARPOL, Load Line and SOLAS Conventions.

7.1.3   The FPSO and the FSU present similar hazards to personnel and the environment, although the inclusion of production facilities on the FPSO serves to increase the risk associated with any marine incident.

7.1.4   The loading of an oil tanker at a FPSO or FSU may be conducted in a number of different ways, depending on the design of the facility which, in turn, will be driven by the physical and environmental conditions at the site of the installation. FPSOs and FSUs are configured to discharge either via a single point or buoy mooring, in a side by side (SBS) configuration or via a tandem mooring arrangement.

7.1.5   Offtake or export oil tankers may be specialist dedicated shuttle tankers or conventional trading oil tankers. Dedicated shuttle tankers tend to load over the bow whereas a conventional oil tanker, which is not equipped with the special fittings of the shuttle tanker, generally loads by means of a hose attached to its midship manifold.

7.1.6   Cargo operations may be conducted by connecting floating or submerged hoses, fixed arms or conventional cargo hoses between the cargo manifold on board the FPSO, FSU or buoy and the oil tanker manifold in such a way as to permit the transfer of oil without leakage. The oil tanker manifold may be situated at the bow, the stern or either side amidships. The operation should always be controlled so as to prevent any escape or spillage.

7.2   FPSO and FSU mooring arrangements

7.2.1   The mooring arrangement of the FPSO/FSU will be determined by a number of factors that include:

.1   meteorological and oceanographic (metocean) conditions;

.2   the need to disconnect and reconnect due to weather or other emergency, and

.3   other environmental conditions, such as sea ice.

7.2.2   The FPSO/FSU will be held on station by one, or a combination, of the following:

.1   by means of a spread mooring system, with the FPSO/FSU orientated into the predominant weather and environmental forces in order to minimize vessel motions, such as, excessive rolling;

.2   by means of a fixed, rigid connection to an internal or external turret or a catenary anchor leg mooring (CALM) buoy, with the FPSO/FSU free to weathervane;

.3   by means of a soft mooring connection to a CALM type buoy;

.4   by a soft yoke mooring to a jacket structure, with the FPSO/FSU free to weathervane;

.5   by means of a differentiated compliance anchoring system (DICAS), this being a mooring system with variable mooring line stiffness at the bow and/or stern of the FPSO/FSU, allowing the FPSO/FSU to partially weathervane; or

.6   by being dynamically positioned (DP) where the only connection to the subsea system is via the production risers.

7.2.3   The mooring arrangement will, in turn, have an impact on the type of cargo handling/ loading arrangement that will be in place. The availability and type of export oil tankers to be employed will also impact on the cargo transfer loading arrangements.

7.2.4   The selection of the mooring arrangement for the FPSO or FSU and subsequent discharge arrangement(s) will be made by the project team early in the design process, balancing the risks posed by environmental conditions against the cost of the technical solution.

7.3   FPSO and FSU offloading arrangements

7.3.1   The offloading of an FPSO and FSU may be undertaken remotely from the unit using a buoy mooring or at the FPSO/FSU, either by tandem mooring or side by side. The choice of system will be subject to a number of factors, including:

.1   regulatory/class/local requirements;

.2   the mooring system; and

.3   offtake oil tanker availability/selection.

Figure 11 – *Tandem mooring arrangement (Source OCIMF)*

7.3.2   Conventional oil tankers are likely to be used for buoy loading – single point mooring (SPM) or multi buoy mooring (MBM) – operations and also for tandem loading where environmental conditions permit. Dedicated shuttle tankers are likely to be used where required by either local regulatory requirements and/or the harsh environment.

7.3.3   Tankers may require tug assistance during the offtake operation to assist with berthing and maintaining position, and during departure. Pull back tugs may be employed to prevent the oil tanker from "riding up" on the buoy or FPSO/FSU and to provide heading control, preventing the tanker from "fishtailing". Shuttle tankers that are equipped with a Dynamic Positioning (DP) system may not require external assistance except in very extreme environments.

7.3.4   Hose handling boats may be employed to convey the hose and mooring hawser from the FPSO/FSU to the tanker during connection.

7.4   Risk management

7.4.1   Risk management of FPSO/FSU operations is addressed in detail in the following publications:

.1   *Guideline for managing marine risks associated with F(P)SOs – (International Association of Oil & Gas Producers – OGP);*

.2   *Tandem offtake guidelines volumes 1 & 2 –* (United Kingdom Offshore Operators Association – UKOOA);

.3   *Offshore loading safety guidelines with special relevance to harsh weather zones –* (OCIMF);

.4   *Tandem mooring and offloading guidelines for conventional tankers at F(P)SO facilities –* (OCIMF); and

.5   *Competence assurance guidelines for F(P)SOs –* (OCIMF)

7.4.2   Operations at FPSOs and FSUs involving transfer to an oil tanker moored at a SPM, MBM or CALM buoy are essentially the same as at other buoy moorings, as described in chapter 5 of this manual.

7.4.3   Tandem moored offtake operations

7.4.3.1   The risk of pollution during tandem offloading from a FPSO or FSU to either a conventional oil tanker or a shuttle tanker arises from a number of operations and potential events:

.1   damage to hose during deployment and recovery;

.2   disconnection of hose from the oil tanker's manifold;

.3   mooring hawser failure;

.4   cargo hose failure;

.5   cargo hose over pressurization;

.6   oil tanker contact with FPSO/FSU due to ranging;

.7   oil tanker breakout due to weather or current induced fishtailing; and

.8   loss of oil tanker motive power causing excessive strain on mooring hawser and subsequent breakout.

7.4.4   Side by side offtake operations

7.4.4.1   The risk of pollution during side by side offloading from a FPSO or FSU to either a conventional oil tanker or a shuttle tanker arises from a number of operations and potential events:

.1   damage to hose during deployment and recovery;

.2   disconnection of hose from the oil tanker's manifold;

.3   cargo hose failure;

.4   cargo hose over pressurization;

.5   risk of contact during the mooring procedure – minimized by the use of suitably sized fenders and adequate tug support;

.6   risk of contact between the upper parts of the vessels as a result of excessive rolling in a beam swell;

.7   offtake oil tanker breakout due to mooring line failure.

7.4.4.2   An operations manual and procedures will be in place on the FPSO/FSU with the aim of minimizing the risk of pollution. Elements of these procedures will need to be communicated to the offtake oil tanker by the FPSO or FSU.

7.5   Tandem moored offtake operations at FPSOs and FSUs

7.5.1   Mooring arrangements

7.5.1.1   The mooring arrangements required for a tandem moored offtake (offloading) operation are as detailed in chapter 5 of this manual for mooring at a SPM. The FPSO or FSU will provide hawser(s), chafe chain(s) and pick-up rope(s) and the offtake oil tanker should be provided with one or more bow chain stoppers. Full details of required arrangements are provided in the OCIMF publication *Recommendations for equipment employed in the bow mooring of conventional tankers at single point moorings*.

7.5.2   Hose arrangements

7.5.2.1   FPSO/FSU cargo hose systems for transferring cargo to a tandem moored offtake oil tanker are similar to those used at conventional SPMs. The floating cargo hose system is designed to provide a flexible oil flow path between the FPSO or FSU and the offtake oil tanker. The primary differences between a SPM system and a FPSO or FSU system are:

.1   designing the cargo hose system to avoid chafing of the first lengths off the FPSO or FSU against the unit's hull. A method to facilitate this is to locate the connecting flange (facing down) outboard of the rail, i.e. allowing the cargo hose to be suspended vertically from the manifold; and

.2   cargo hose systems should be designed to provide a smooth transition into the water from the FPSO or FSU. This can be facilitated by the use of reinforced carcass hoses and, in some systems, by the use of snubbing wires.

7.5.2.2   The hoses used for the transfer of crude oils or petroleum products should be specially designed and constructed for the product being handled and the purpose for which they are being used. Hoses should comply with relevant international standards and bear the following durable indelible markings:

.1   the manufacturer's name or trademark;

.2   identification of the standard specification for manufacture;

.3   factory test pressure (note: equal to rated working pressure, maximum working pressure, maximum allowable working pressure);

.4   month and year of manufacture and the manufacturer's serial number;

.5   indication that the hose is electrically continuous or electrically discontinuous, semi-continuous or anti-static; and

.6   the type of service for which it is intended, e.g. oil or chemical.

7.5.2.3   Test data with respect to each hose should be available and should be sighted prior to the hose being used for transfer.

7.5.2.4   Hoses should be withdrawn from service and retired against defined criteria, which may include the following:

.1   the presence of defects detected during visual inspections. Defects prompting retirement could include irregularities in the outside diameter, such as kinking, damaged or exposed reinforcement or permanent deformation of the casing and damage, slippage or misalignment of end fittings;

.2   after a defined period in service, established in consultation with the manufacturer; and

.3   when the temporary elongation of the hose, measured during routine pressure tests, exceeds maximum allowable values.

7.5.2.5 A visual inspection of each of the hose assemblies should be carried out before they are connected to the manifold to determine that they are free of damage. If damage to a hose or flange is present, the hose should be withdrawn from use for further inspection, repair or retirement.

7.5.2.6 Depending on their design, the elements of each hose assembly should meet the following requirements:

.1   threaded couplings should ensure the security of connection without any additional fixing arrangements;

.2   flanged joints should meet the requirements of international standards for connecting sizes, and their material and design should correspond to accepted standards; and

.3   quick release couplings should meet the requirements of international standards for connecting sizes. Their material and design should correspond to accepted standards.

7.5.2.7 Cargo hoses should be properly stowed or otherwise secured between cargo transfer operations. Cargo hose stowage methods should take into account the properties of the hose that is intended to be utilized, e.g. the diameter of a stowage reel must be compatible with the construction and stiffness of the hose.

7.6   Side by side offtake operations at FPSOs and FSUs

7.6.1   General

7.6.1.1 Side by side (SBS) cargo transfers from a FPSO or FSU to an export oil tanker are suitable for sheltered areas with restricted sea room and are not suitable for exposed locations where heavy seas and/or strong winds are a feature.

7.6.1.2 The offtake oil tanker is moored directly alongside the FPSO separated by floating rubber fenders, and cargo transfer is through flexible rubber hoses directly connected to the manifold of each vessel.

7.6.1.3 Although the ICS/OCIMF publication *Ship-to-ship transfer guide – petroleum* provides an excellent reference for SBS operations, moored FPSOs and FSUs present specific problems that are not common in general ship-to ship-transfers. One principal difference is that the FPSO or FSU is permanently moored and the mooring manoeuvre cannot be made "underway" with both vessels steaming. A second difference is that the mooring chains of catenary anchored FPSOs or FSUs tend to extend beyond the hull and are a consideration when berthing and unberthing the offtake oil tankers. As a result of these differences, tug assistance will normally be required during the mooring and unmooring operation of the offtake oil tanker alongside the FPSO or FSU.

7.6.2 Hose arrangements

7.6.2.1 The hoses used for the side by side transfer of crude oils or petroleum products should be specially designed and constructed for the product being handled and the purpose for which they are being used. The recommendations given in 7.5.2 above for the marking, inspection, testing, withdrawal from service and make-up of assemblies are applicable to hoses used for side by side transfers.

7.7 Offtake tanker operations

7.7.1 All pollution prevention measures normally taken while alongside a jetty are applicable when an oil tanker is at a FPSO or FSU installation. The mooring arrangements should be capable of accommodating the largest oil tanker likely to use the facility in all conditions of sea and weather that can be reasonably expected, at which the oil tanker can be safely afloat, and to and from which the oil tanker can at all times safely proceed with sufficient under keel clearance. During the time the oil tanker is moored at the facility, frequent and regular inspection of mooring lines and cargo hoses is essential. Excessive movement of the oil tanker may cause rupture of the ship's connections to the FPSO, FSU or buoy. Cargo hoses must not be subjected to mooring forces.

7.7.2 The following basic principles should be applied if pollution is to be avoided:

.1   all personnel concerned with the loading or discharge of oil should be fully aware of the need to prevent pollution;

.2   all personnel should adhere strictly to the joint plan of operations including the provision of an efficient communication system;

Figure 12 – *Tandem mooring configuration (Source OCIMF)*

.3 the responsible persons should check the items listed in paragraph 7.9.3 before the oil actually flows;

.4 all personnel involved should be aware of the immediate measures and response necessary in the event of an escape of oil; and

.5 all equipment, the failure of which might result in an escape of oil, should be inspected and tested regularly.

7.8 Control and communications

7.8.1 The FPSO or FSU should have a centre from which the operation is controlled.

7.8.2 The centre should be equipped with radio or telephone, ensuring reliable two-way communications by voice between the responsible person in the centre and the responsible person on the oil tanker. The communications shall be in an agreed language understood by both persons.

7.8.3 Means shall be provided for control of the operations and for emergency stopping of the flow.

7.9   Preparation for operations

7.9.1   The Master of the oil tanker should be fully advised of the availability of tugs and mooring craft, and of any particular features of the FPSO/FSU facility. He should also be advised of any local regulations regarding pollution.

7.9.2   A joint plan of operation should be developed on the basis of information exchanged between the oil tanker and the control centre, comprising the following:

.1   mooring arrangements;

.2   quantities and characteristics of the cargo(es) to be loaded and identification of any toxic components;

.3   sequence of loading tanks;

.4   details of cargo transfer system, number of pumps and maximum permissible pressure;

.5   rate of oil transfer during operations (initial, maximum and topping-up);

.6   the time required for starting, stopping and changing rate of delivery during topping-off of tanks;

.7   normal stopping and emergency shutdown procedures;

.8   disposition and quantity of ballast and slops, and disposal if applicable;

.9   maximum draught and freeboard anticipated during operation;

.10   details of proposed method of venting or inerting cargo tanks;

.11   details of crude oil washing, if applicable;

.12   emergency and oil spill containment procedures;

.13   sequence of actions in case of spillage of oil;

.14   environmental and operational limits that would trigger suspension of loading and disconnection of the oil tanker from the unit;

.15   specific conditions of operations (if any); and

.16   local or government rules that apply to the transfer.

7.9.3 Before commencement of operations the responsible persons should ensure:

.1 proper mooring of the offtake oil tanker;

.2 joint completion of appropriate pre-transfer checklist(s);

.3 sufficient personnel available for safe performance of operation;

.4 availability of reliable communication between FPSO/FSU control centre and oil tanker;

.5 proper connection and securing of hoses to the offtake oil tanker's manifold;

.6 proper condition and position of hoses, hose saddles and supports;

.7 that flange joints, where used, are fully bolted and sealed;

.8 proper blanking of unused cargo and bunker connections;

.9 any valve through which oil could be discharged to the sea is closed and inspected and, if not used in the operation, is sealed to ensure that it is not inadvertently opened;

.10 deck scuppers on the offtake oil tanker and the FPSO/FSU are properly plugged;

.11 availability of empty drip trays on the offtake oil tanker and the FPSO/FSU under couplings of hoses, and means for drip tray drainage;

.12 availability of materials on the offtake tanker and the FPSO/FSU for on-deck clean-up in case of spillage;

.13 proper illumination of working places and equipment involved in the operation;

.14 deck watches are established on the offtake oil tanker and FPSO/FSU to pay particular attention to moorings, hoses and manifold integrity; and

.15 correct understanding of commands and signals by the responsible person on the oil tanker during operations and in emergency situations.

7.9.4   The operation may be started only after the responsible person on the oil tanker and the responsible person in the FPSO/FSU control centre have agreed to do so, either verbally or in writing.

7.10   Performance of operations

7.10.1   The operation should be started at a slow rate in order to ensure that all connections and hoses are tight, the oil is being directed into intended pipelines and tanks, no excessive pressure is being built up in the hoses and pipelines, and there is no evidence of oil leakage in way of the oil tanker's hull.

7.10.2   Only after being satisfied that there is no leakage, the oil is being transferred into the intended pipelines and tanks, and there is no excessive pressure, may the rate of transfer be increased up to the maximum indicated in the plan of operation.

7.10.3   The responsible persons on the offtake oil tanker and the FPSO/FSU should periodically check the following and, if necessary, take appropriate remedial action:

> **.1**   for any leakage from the equipment and system, or through the oil tanker's plating;
>
> **.2**   that there is no leakage into pump rooms, ballast or void spaces or cargo tanks not scheduled to be loaded;
>
> **.3**   if there is any excessive pressure in piping and hoses;
>
> **.4**   the mooring arrangements;
>
> **.5**   the condition of hoses and their support arrangements; and
>
> **.6**   tank ullages and quantities transferred.

7.10.4   Care must be taken to prevent surge pressures during loading when changing over tanks on the offtake oil tanker. The filling valves of the next tanks in sequence should be opened before the valves on the tank being filled are closed.

7.10.5   Information on quantities transferred should be routinely and regularly exchanged between the offtake oil tanker and the FPSO/FSU control centre. Any significant discrepancies between the quantity discharged and the quantity received should be promptly investigated.

7.10.6   The responsible persons should collaborate regarding necessary changes in mooring arrangements.

7.11 Completion of operations

7.11.1 During offtake oil tanker loading operations, it should be ensured that adequate ullage space is left in each tank being filled. When it is required to stop cargo transfer operations, the responsible person should advise the FPSO/FSU control room in ample time. When non return valves are not fitted, all necessary precautions should be taken to prevent oil flowing back into the offtake oil tanker.

7.11.2 Before hoses are disconnected, they should be drained as far as is practical and any residual product should be contained in the manifold drip tray. Following disconnection, the hose should be securely blanked.

7.11.3 As soon as practicable after the transfer operation has been completed, and before unmooring, the responsible persons should ensure that all valves in the systems are closed and that the offtake oil tanker's cargo tank openings are closed and secured for sea.

7.12 Suspension of operations

7.12.1 Operations should be suspended when:

.1 wind and sea conditions exceed the permissible limits for safe operations;

.2 movement of the offtake oil tanker reaches the maximum permissible and may risk damaging hoses;

.3 there is a failure of the main communication system between the offtake oil tanker and the FPSO/FSU control centre and there are no proper standby communications;

.4 there is a power failure on the offtake oil tanker or FPSO/FSU;

.5 any escape of oil into the sea is discovered;

.6 there is an unexplained pressure drop in the cargo system;

.7 fire danger is discovered;

.8 any oil leakage is discovered from hoses, couplings and deck pipelines on the FPSO/FSU or offtake oil tanker;

.9 overflow of oil onto the deck occurs caused by overfilling a cargo tank;

.10 any faults or damage threatening the escape of oil are discovered;

> **.11** there is a failure of illumination or poor visibility at the location; and
>
> **.12** there is a significant, unexplained difference between the quantities of cargo delivered and received.

7.12.2 Operations may be resumed only after the weather and seas have abated or appropriate remedial action has been taken.

7.13 FPSO and FSU operations while disconnected from their mooring system

7.13.1 Some FPSOs and FSUs have the capability to be disconnected from their mooring system while at their operational location and some may also be self-propelled. It may be necessary for the FPSO/FSU to disconnect and move off location to avoid environmental conditions/loads that exceed the design capabilities and limits of the FPSO/FSU while on location. Additionally, FPSOs/FSUs may need to be taken off location for drydocking, repair or maintenance work.

7.13.2 To ensure that disconnectable and self-propelled FPSOs and FSUs can be readily and efficiently disconnected, they should have a level of safety equivalent to that afforded by the SOLAS and Load Line Conventions.

7.13.3 The application of SOLAS chapter IX and the ISM Code to self-propelled and readily disconnectable FPSOs and FSUs is recommended to establish an effective safety management system and to ensure integration of the marine staff. Measures should include an effective maintenance programme, particularly for essential marine systems and equipment, and a process to ensure that the competence of marine personnel is maintained at an adequate level.

7.14 References

The International Safety Management Code (ISM Code) – (IMO)

International safety guide for oil tankers and terminals (ISGOTT) – (IAPH/ICS/OCIMF)

Ship-to-ship transfer guide – petroleum – (ICS and OCIMF)

Recommendations for equipment employed in the bow mooring of conventional tankers at single point moorings – (OCIMF)

Guide to manufacturing and purchasing hoses for offshore moorings – (OCIMF)

Guidelines for the handling, storage, inspection and testing of hoses in the field – (OCIMF)

SPM hose ancillary equipment guide – (OCIMF)

Recommendations for oil tanker manifolds and associated equipment – (OCIMF)

Guideline for managing marine risks associated with F(P)SOs – (The International Association of Oil & Gas Producers – OGP)

Tandem offtake guidelines volumes 1 & 2 – (United Kingdom Offshore Operators Association – UKOOA)

Offshore loading safety guidelines with special relevance to harsh weather zones – (OCIMF)

Tandem mooring and offloading guidelines for conventional tankers at FPSO facilities – (OCIMF)

Competence assurance guidelines for F(P)SOs – (OCIMF)

Chapter 8
Oil tanker operations in ice covered waters

8.1 Recommendations to ships operating in ice covered waters

8.1.1 The *United Nations Convention on the Law of the Sea (UNCLOS)* Article 234 states that: "Coastal States have the right to adopt and enforce non discriminatory laws and regulations for the prevention, reduction and control of marine pollution from vessels in ice covered areas within the limits of the exclusive economic zone, where particularly severe climatic conditions and the presence of ice covering such areas for most of the year create obstructions or exceptional hazards to navigation, and pollution of the marine environment could cause major harm to or irreversible disturbance of the ecological balance. Such laws and regulations shall have due regard to navigation and the protection and preservation of the marine environment based on the best available scientific evidence."

Figure 13 – *Ship operating in ice covered waters (Source OCIMF)*

8.1.2   Ice covered waters can be broadly subdivided between polar ice covered waters with the most severe weather conditions and other ice covered waters. According to IMO's *Guidelines for ships operating in polar waters*, adopted on 2 December 2009 by resolution A.1024(26), the following definitions are applicable:

.1   *polar waters* includes both Arctic and Antarctic waters;

.2   *waters* means those waters which are located north of a line extending from latitude 58°00′.0N, longitude 042°00′.0W to latitude 64°37′.0N, longitude 035°27′.0W and thence by a rhumb line to latitude 67°03′.9N, longitude 026°33′.4W and thence by a rhumb line to Sørkapp, Jan Mayen and by the southern shore of Jan Mayen to the Island of Bjørnøya and thence by a great circle line from the Island of Bjørnøya to Cap Kanin Nos and thence by the northern shore of the Asian continent eastward to the Bering Strait and thence from the Bering Strait westward to latitude 60°N as far as Il'pyrskiy and following the 60th North parallel eastward as far as and including Etolin Strait and thence by the northern shore of the North American continent as far south as latitude 60°N and thence eastward along parallel of latitude 60°N, to longitude 56°37′.1W and thence to the latitude 58°00′.0N, longitude 042°00′.0W;

.3   *Antarctic waters* means those waters that are south of 60°S; and

.4   *ice covered waters* means polar waters where local ice conditions present a structural risk to a ship.

8.1.3   Ships operating in ice covered waters, particularly in the Polar environment, are exposed to a number of unique risks. Poor weather conditions and the relative lack of good charts, communication systems and other navigational aids pose challenges for mariners. The remoteness of the areas makes rescue or clean-up operations difficult and costly. Cold temperatures may reduce the effectiveness of numerous components of the ship, ranging from deck machinery and emergency equipment to sea suctions. Where ice is present, it can impose additional loads on the hull, propulsion systems and fittings.

8.1.4   The *Guidelines for ships operating in polar waters*, address the fact that the polar environment imposes additional demands on ship systems, including navigation, communications, life saving, main and auxiliary machinery. They emphasize the need to ensure that all ship systems are capable of functioning effectively under anticipated operating conditions and that adequate levels of safety in accident and emergency situations are provided. In addition, the guidelines recognize that safe operation in such conditions requires specific attention to human factors, including training and operational procedures.

8.1.5   These guidelines for ships operating in ice covered waters, including polar ice covered waters, are intended to address those additional provisions deemed necessary for consideration beyond existing requirements of the SOLAS and MARPOL Conventions, in order to take into account the climatic conditions and to meet appropriate standards of maritime safety and pollution prevention. IMO resolution A.1024(26) invites all governments concerned to give effect to the guidelines for ships constructed on or after 1 January 2011 and to give effect to the guidelines for ships constructed before 1 January 2011, as far as is reasonable and practicable. A mandatory polar code is being developed that will supersede these guidelines once adopted.

8.1.6   Not all ships which enter ice covered waters will be able to navigate safely in all areas at all times of the year. All ships and the equipment to be carried in accordance with the guidelines should be designed, constructed, and maintained in compliance with applicable national standards (ice classifications) of the Administration or the appropriate requirements of a recognized organization which provide an equivalent level of safety for its intended service. A system of ice classification of ships has been developed to designate different levels of capability.

8.2   Ice classification rules

8.2.1   As expressed in the *Helsinki Commission (HELCOM) Recommendation 25/7*, the approximate equivalence of the ice classes of different classification societies with the Finnish-Swedish Ice Class Rules is based on the comparison of hull structural requirements. Equivalence is estimated on the condition that the hull structural strength given by the rules of a classification society is on a similar level as the hull structural strength obtained by applying the Finnish-Swedish Ice Class Rules. It is the responsibility of the owner to select an appropriate polar class.

8.2.2   In addition, the requirements of the applicable classification and flag States regarding the power of the main engines should be fulfilled. Alternatively, the ship should have sufficient power for possible independent movement at a minimum steady speed of 1–2 knots through level ice of a thickness, depending on the ice class of the ship.

8.2.3   In parallel, the International Association of Classification Societies (IACS) has developed a set of Unified Requirements which, in addition to general classification society rules, address all essential aspects of construction for ships of Polar Class.

8.2.4   Ships that comply with the IACS Unified Requirements I2 and I3 can be considered for a Polar Class notation as listed in Table 8.1. These requirements are in addition to the open water requirements of each member society.

8.2.5   Ships that are also to receive an "icebreaker" notation may have additional requirements and are to receive special consideration. "Icebreaker" refers to any ship having an operational profile that includes escort or ice management functions, having powering and dimensions that allow it to undertake aggressive operations in ice covered waters.

8.2.6   The Polar Class notation is used throughout the IACS Unified Requirements for Polar Ships to convey the differences between classes with respect to operational capability and strength.

Table 8.1 – *IACS Polar Class descriptions*

Polar Class	General description
PC 1	Year-round operation in all ice covered waters.
PC 2	Year-round operation in moderate multi year ice conditions.
PC 3	Year-round operation in second year ice, which may include multi-year ice inclusions.
PC 4	Year-round operation in thick first year ice, which may include old ice inclusions.
PC 5	Year-round operation in medium first year ice, which may include old ice inclusions.
PC 6	Summer/autumn operation in medium first year ice, which may include old ice inclusions.
PC 7	Summer/autumn operation in thin first year ice, which may include old ice inclusions.

Note: In the table above, ice descriptions follow the World Meteorological Organization (WMO) sea ice nomenclature

8.2.7   Operations in ice covered waters should take due account of factors that include ship class, environmental conditions, icebreaker escort, prepared tracks, short or local routes, crew experience, support technology and services such as ice mapping, communications, ports of refuge, repair facilities and other ships in convoy.

8.3 Ice navigator

8.3.1 The crewing of all ships in ice covered waters should take account of the provisions listed here, and also of the relative lack of shore and support infrastructure which may be available to assist in any operations.

8.3.2 As many as possible of the ship's deck and engine officers should be trained in ship operations in ice covered waters.

8.3.3 All ships operating in ice covered waters should carry at least one qualified ice navigator who will continuously monitor ice conditions at all times while the ship is underway and making way in the presence of ice. Consideration should also be given to carrying an ice navigator when planning voyages into polar or ice covered waters.

8.3.4 *Ice navigator* means any individual who, in addition to being qualified under the STCW Convention, is specially trained and otherwise qualified to direct the movement of a ship in ice covered waters. Qualifications of an ice navigator should include documentary evidence of having completed on-the-job training, as appropriate, and may include simulation training.

8.3.5 The ice navigator should have documentary evidence of having satisfactorily completed a nationally approved or industry recognized approved training programme in ice navigation. Such a training programme should provide knowledge, understanding and proficiency required for operating a ship in ice covered waters, including recognition of ice formation and characteristics; ice indications; ice manoeuvring; use of ice forecasts, atlases and codes; hull stress caused by ice; ice escort operations; ice breaking operations and effect of ice accretion on vessel stability. Some additional requirements may be established by national Administrations.

8.4 Anchoring and towing

8.4.1 All Polar Class ships navigating in ice covered waters should be capable of anchoring and providing limited assistance in the case of disabling damage or breakdown, towards the prevention of a catastrophic loss or pollution incident. The capability of ships to provide assistance should be considered of prime importance, having due regard to the lack of repair facilities, the limited number of dedicated towing ships available, and the response time that may be required by a dedicated towing ship to be able to provide effective assistance in ice covered waters. Reference should be made to guidance published by IMO with regard to the anchoring and towing arrangements of Polar Class ships.

8.5   Safety requirements

8.5.1   Ice surveillance systems

8.5.1.1   Safe navigation in ice covered waters is impossible without adequate information about ice conditions. Such information can be obtained from national and international ice services and is also available through selected commercial vendors.

8.5.1.2   Experience of navigation in ice conditions has proved the importance of ice information and other hydro-meteorological support providing safety and efficiency of sea operations. The currently available ice information system is based on combined processing and analysis of non homogeneous information from satellites, ground based observations, autonomous drifting buoys and polar stations, as well as icebreakers and ships.

8.5.1.3   Information about ice conditions is published in the form of ice charts, ice reports, electronic data presentations, or bulletins. Details about ice conditions contain information on the location of the boundary of the ice field and open water, the edge of the ice field with thickness exceeding 10 cm, the thickness of level ice, ice concentration, and ice ridge fields along the routes to the ports used during the winter period. The terms and symbols of WMO are used when describing ice and ice conditions. In some countries, ice reporting can also contain information about traffic restrictions, information about traffic control, and the location of the assisting icebreakers and their operational area.

8.5.1.4   Contact information for the national ice services (and basic information about ice) can be obtained from their websites. Also, see the References section at the end of this chapter.

8.5.2   Traffic restrictions based on safety aspects

8.5.2.1   The national Administrations set traffic restrictions based on safety aspects for ships sailing in ice conditions. Adequate ice strengthening is required for ships sailing in ice in accordance with paragraph 8.2. More stringent traffic restrictions may also be set based on operational reasons.

8.5.2.2   The traffic restrictions for the Baltic Sea area are based on the measured level ice thickness, or the calculated level ice thickness in the coastal area (see *HELCOM Recommendation 25/7 on Safety of Winter Navigation in the Baltic Sea Area* containing *Guidelines for the Safety of Winter Navigation in the Baltic Sea Area*). This guidance includes procedures for the escorting of certain vessels and the provision of icebreaker support.

8.5.2.3 The traffic restrictions can be eased and finally removed after the melting period of ice has started in spring and the strength of the level ice fields has started to decrease.

8.5.2.4 The Administration may grant an exemption from the traffic restrictions on an individual ship, which does not have the required ice class, if a detailed analysis of the strength of the vessel in the prevailing ice conditions is made. In the analysis the level of ice thickness, strength, pressure, coverage and other relevant information on ice conditions should be taken into account. The ship owner should submit to the Port Authority or to the Administration a written document, developed by a competent organization, specifying admissible speeds of ship under various ice conditions, the number of required assisting icebreakers, and other relevant operational information. This information should also be submitted to the icebreakers responsible for icebreaker assistance in the area.

8.5.3   Winterization of ships

8.5.3.1 A ship's ice class notation covers the vessel's structural strength, propulsion power and arrangements. The notation does not cover suitability from the standpoint of commercial operability in low temperatures, ice navigation and/or icebreaker escort. Some ice class ships may have additional notations, generally referred to as "winterization" or "de-ice" notations. These notations will embrace technical and operational issues to minimize risk when operating in ice or severe cold conditions.

8.5.3.2 A ship should be adapted for safe operation at a low outdoor air temperature down to minus 30°C. This concerns the operability of the material of hull structures, deck equipment (anchor handling and mooring, towing and cargo handling), main engine cooling systems, material of propeller and its sufficient immersion to reduce interaction with ice. Ship operators should have written procedures addressing risk minimization when preparing for and operating in cold weather and ice.

8.5.3.3 The stability of ships at a low outdoor air temperature under open water conditions should be demonstrated to be sufficient taking into account the probability of icing.

8.5.4   Ship operational control

8.5.4.1 The ship should not be operated outside the worst intended conditions and design limitations.

8.6 Operating and training manuals

8.6.1 The operating manual, or supplementary manual in the case of ships not normally operating in ice covered waters, should contain at least the following information on issues directly related to operations in such waters. With respect to contingency planning in the event that the ship suffers ice damage, the manual should conform to guidelines developed by the IMO.

8.6.2 For Polar Class ships, the operating manual should include the supplementary information, in clearly defined chapters specified by the Administration.

8.6.3 Regarding information on machinery or system failures, guidance should take into account the results of any risk or failure analysis reports developed during the ship design.

8.6.4 The training manual should cover all aspects of ship operation in ice covered waters listed below, plus other related information considered necessary by the Administration:

.1 summary of the guidelines for ships operating in ice covered and polar waters;

.2 ice recognition;

.3 navigation in ice; and

.4 escorted operation.

8.6.5 The *Drills and Emergency Instructions* information should be incorporated as annexes to the manual.

The ship's owner/operator should ensure that any additional documentation referenced in the training manual is fully understood by those on board the ship for all operations in polar ice covered waters, noting also that applicable national legislation should be complied with.

8.7 Environmental protection

8.7.1 Reference should be made to guidance published by the Organization regarding provisions concerning environmental protection and damage control equipment. These take due regard to the lack of waste reception and repair facilities, communication limitations, unique navigational and environmental hazards, and limited response capabilities of available assistance in ice covered waters, noting the IMO prohibition of fuel oil in Antarctic waters, as subsequently amended.

8.7.2   All hoses used to transfer potentially polluting cargoes from the ship to another ship or to shore should have the connection between the hose and the hose couplings made in an efficient and strong fashion to minimize the possibility of pollution due to failure of this connection. Hose connection and management should always follow industry best practice. Couplings between hose sections should be capable of being securely locked together to prevent inadvertent disconnection and hose integrity should be established prior to transfer of pollutants.

8.7.3   Hoses and flexible pipes should be manufactured out of materials retaining adequate strength and elasticity characteristics at the minimum anticipated temperature.

8.7.4   The Shipboard Oil Pollution Emergency Plan (SOPEP), required in accordance with the MARPOL Convention, shall be developed taking into particular account ice covered waters and polar waters, as required.

8.7.5   Oil spill countermeasures in ice infested waters

8.7.5.1 All ships navigating in ice covered or polar waters shall be adequately equipped and their crews properly trained to provide effective response actions in case of incidents. All ships should have the capability to contain and clean up minor deck and overside spills.

8.7.5.2 To be prepared to respond to oil spills in remote areas, an effective oil spill contingency plan and appropriate oil combating technique are required. Oil spill response system and methods used in open water (vessels, skimmers, booms, etc) are the generally accepted approach. However, their use is not always applicable in ice covered waters. Oil spill response in ice covered waters is much more complex than in open waters. An impact assessment carried out using a risk-based approach must be undertaken and suitable response strategies developed to mitigate any environmental impact of any oil spill.

8.8   Vessel Traffic Management Information System (VTMIS) and Ship/Response Vessel System (Servs)

8.8.1   In ice conditions, an important role of the Ship Reporting System (SRS) is to provide information on way points for ships sailing in the area. The organization responsible for defining and providing information on way points should be identified by each country and only one organization should be authorized for this purpose. The national SRS Centres should create clear procedures for the distribution of information on way points to ships, national Vessel Traffic Service (VTS) Centres and other SRS Centres.

8.8.2 The Administrations should set operational instructions for ships sailing in ice covered waters. Such instructions should contain the following:

.1 instructions for sailing alone in ice;

.2 instructions for sailing in ice under icebreaker supervision; and

.3 instructions for sailing assisted by an icebreaker: escorting, in towing, and sailing in a convoy headed by an icebreaker.

8.9 Preparing ships for sailing in ice covered waters

8.9.1 For sailing in ice conditions where the danger of meeting heavy ice and hull damage constantly exists, and with the aim to decrease the possibility of oil pollution, it is necessary to use ice strengthened ships, which are in full compliance with the requirements of MARPOL, National Classification Societies, IACS Unified Requirements for "Polar Ships" and appropriate national or regional legislation.

8.9.2 A ship intended for service in ice covered waters must have the appropriate certificates and documents to sail in the anticipated ice conditions. Some Administrations may require an "ice passport" to be issued. In the absence of these documents, the Master of the ship should timely inform the Administration of the country prior to entering its ice covered waters. The Administration may consider the possibility of including such ship into a convoy for ice escort.

8.9.3 If there is an alternative route around the ice, even if it is considerably longer, it is safer for an unstrengthened ship, or for a ship whose structural capability does not match the prevailing ice conditions, to take it rather than going through a large amount of ice. Any expected savings of fuel will be more than offset by the risk of damage and the actual fuel consumption may be higher going through ice, even if the distance is shorter.

8.9.4 Before a laden ship enters the ice, especially a tanker, all openings in spaces such as the forepeak, aft peak, double bottom, fuel oil tanks and cargo tanks should be properly closed, and watertight doors secured. The watertight compartments should be kept closed during the entire time the ship is in ice as, in the event of damage to the ship's hull, the sealed compartments may assist in preserving the ship's buoyancy, and thus prevent or mitigate any consequent damage to the environment. A light ship should be ballasted down to ice draught, if appropriate, or to such a draft that would offer protection to a bulbous bow, rudder, or propeller.

8.9.5   While sailing in ice, it is recommended that sufficient ullage is available in cargo tanks to enable cargo to be transferred internally in the event of a tank being damaged. This recommendation does not apply to double hulled ice class tankers.

8.9.6   It is recommended that ships carry a submersible pump and hoses to facilitate the emergency transfer of cargo from a damaged tank into other tanks or to another ship.

8.9.7   Before the ship enters into ice, it is recommended that a suitable amount of ballast is taken on. Consideration should also be given to transferring fuel oil from forward tanks, if fitted, which are more susceptible to damage when sailing in ice.

8.9.8   Prior to sailing in ice covered or polar waters, it is recommended that drills are held according to the Shipboard Oil Pollution Emergency Plan to address scenarios that include damage control, the closure of hull penetrations and the response to oil leaks into the sea from cargo or fuel oil tanks. The ship's officers must be familiar with the basic provisions associated with their ship's survivability, including actions to be taken to minimize the risk of the ship foundering if damaged and any limitations on internal transfers of cargo or bunkers.

8.10   Sailing in ice

8.10.1   When sailing in ice covered or polar waters, the Master must maintain contact with the appropriate national Ice Management Body in the area and act in strict compliance with their recommendations.

8.10.2   The entry of the ship into ice and its movement in ice is allowed only following permission being granted by the person responsible for ice operations in the area. It is prohibited for a ship to enter into ice without it.

8.10.3   In the absence of conditions providing for the safe entry of a ship, particularly a loaded tanker, into the edge of an ice field from the open sea, the ship is prohibited from entering into the ice. The Master should wait at a safe distance from the ice field edge for an improvement in conditions and report simultaneously to the Captain of the Port or the person responsible for ice operations in the area.

8.10.4   The approach to the ice field edge should be at minimum speed. Once in the ice, speed of transit should take into account the ship's hull strength, cargo characteristics and ice conditions in order to avoid any possibility of hull damage and potential loss of containment.

8.10.5   When entering into ice covered waters, impacts with thick pieces of ice may be unavoidable. Where possible, measures should be taken to prevent heavy ice contact with vulnerable parts of the hull, such as in way of fuel oil deep tanks.

8.10.6   When moving in ice covered waters, sharp changes of course should be avoided, as ice will impact against the bow and stern parts of the hull, where fuel oil tanks are usually located, and damage may be caused through contact with ice piece edges and submerged ice rams.

8.10.7   While sailing in ice, essential equipment required for the emergency transfer of cargo, ballast or bunkers should be maintained in a state of readiness in order to be immediately available in the event of hull damage being sustained.

8.10.8   When sailing in ice, the Master should ensure that the level of oil in cargo and fuel oil tanks is regularly monitored and that the cause of any significant change is immediately investigated and, if necessary, remedial action is taken. The adjacent sea surface and the ship's wake should also be observed to provide an early indication of any oil leak to the sea.

8.10.9   At the first signs of ice compression, every effort should be made to bring the ship out of the area of compact ice or grounded ice hummocks, where the hull is more likely to suffer damage than in broken ice. In the event of imminent damage in the area of tanks containing oil, all possible measures should be taken to eliminate any potential oil spill.

8.10.10   In the event of an oil spill, the Master must act according to the Shipboard Oil Pollution Emergency Plan (SOPEP) and report to the appropriate national Administration and the Captain of the nearest icebreaker, ship and port, while taking all possible measures to stop outflow to the sea and minimize pollution.

8.11   Transfer of oil in ice covered waters

8.11.1   Non routine transfer of oil in ice covered waters should, where possible, be avoided as the first priority. All oil transfer operations in ice covered waters can be made only after notification and receiving permission of local authorities, persons in charge of supplier and recipient vessels or facilities. Before the transfer process the use of an effective checklist is recommended, and an example is shown in the appendix. It is important that all parties involved in the transfer are aware of the various actions required during the operation.

Figure 14 – *Vessel operating in ice covered waters (Source OCIMF)*

8.11.2 Transfer operations should be conducted in full compliance with the recommended safe practices, such as those contained in chapter 4 of this manual and in the industry publication *International safety guide for oil tankers and terminals*. Particular attention must be paid to:

.1 effectiveness of communications;

.2 ensuring adequate supervision;

.3 security of transfer equipment, hoses and/or arms;

.4 prevention of pollution;

.5 minimization of hazards; and

.6 adequacy of contingency plans and access to response resources.

8.11.3 Up-to-date forecasts of environmental conditions for the transfer location should be available. Limitations for the transfer operation should be defined and may include temperature, visibility, wind force, wind direction, rain, fog, ice, snow, blizzard, sea state or any other relevant environmental parameter. Environmental limits required to suspend transfer operations should be agreed to and noted on the *Ship/Shore Safety Checklist*.

8.11.4 Extreme cold conditions may cause failure of metals, fabrics and plastic parts, rendering them brittle, causing binding or freezing, and impeding the operation of hoses and pumps. In addition, condensation may freeze and create operational problems. All equipment should be inspected for these potential problems and careful oversight maintained during the operation to permit immediate suspension of operations should failure occur or be considered likely to occur.

8.12   References

Safety of winter navigation in the Baltic Sea area – HELCOM Recommendation 25/7 – (Helsinki Commission – HELCOM)

A guide to contingency planning for oil spills on water (International Petroleum Industry Environmental Conservation Association – IPIECA)

Arctic waters oil transfer guidelines – TP 10783 – (Transport Canada)

Arctic Council guidelines for transfer of refined oil and oil products in Arctic waters – TROOP – (Arctic Council)

Further measures to improve the safety of navigation in ice conditions in the Baltic Sea – HELCOM Recommendation 28E/11 – (HELCOM)

Guidelines on bunkering operations and ship-to-ship cargo transfer of oils, subject to MARPOL Annex I, in the Baltic Sea area – HELCOM Recommendation 28/3 – (HELCOM)

International Convention for the Safety of Life at Sea (SOLAS), 1974 – (IMO)

International Convention for the Prevention of Pollution from Ships, 1973, as modified by the Protocol of 1978 relating thereto – (MARPOL Convention) – (IMO)

Manual on Oil Pollution, Section II – Contingency Planning, and Section IV – Combating Oil Spills – (IMO)

Oil and other hazardous substances pollution control, article 1 oil pollution prevention requirements, transfer requirements – (Department of Environmental Conservation, State of Alaska)

Manual on Prevention of Pollution from Ships – RD 31.04.21-97, St. Petersburg, Russia

The guidelines for ships operating in polar waters – (IMO)

IACS Unified Requirements for Polar Ships – (IACS)

International safety guide for oil tankers and terminals (ISGOTT) – (IAPH/ICS/OCIMF).

Regulations for navigation on seaways of Northern Sea Route, Moscow

Winter navigation on the River and Gulf of St. Lawrence, practical notebook for marine engineers and deck officers – TP 14335 – (Transport Canada)

8.13 Relevant industry body websites

Arctic and Antarctic Research Institute	www.aari.nw.ru/index_en.html
Baltic Sea Ice Services	http://www.bsis-ice.dew
Environment Canada, Canadian Ice Service	http://ice-glaces.ec.gc.ca/
United States National Ice Center	www.natice.noaa.gov

Chapter 9
Shore facilities and oil transfer operations
other than at dock areas

9.1   The operation of shoreside facilities, such as oil refineries and storage tank farms, and the use of submarine pipelines could lead to marine pollution. Information regarding this subject is outside the technical mandate of the Organization. However, many documents are available to assist the reader, which have been prepared by organizations with expertise and responsibility in these areas, such as *The international safety guide for oil tanker and terminals* published jointly by ICS, OCIMF and IAPH.

Appendix
Examples of checklists

1   Bunkering safety checklist

2   Example of oil transfer checklist for ice-covered waters

3   Ship/Shore safety checklist

4   Ship-to-ship transfer checklists

1 Bunkering safety checklist (ref ISGOTT Section 25.4.3)

Port _____ Date _____

Ship _____ Barge _____

Master _____ Master _____

1. Bunkers to be transferred

Grade	Tonnes	Volume at loading temperature	Loading temperature	Maximum transfer rate	Maximum line pressure
Fuel oil					
Gas oil/ diesel					
Lubricating oil in bulk					

2. Bunker tanks to be loaded

Tank no.	Grade	Volume of tank @ __%	Vol. of oil in tank before loading	Available volume	Volume to be loaded	Total volumes grade

3. Checks by barge prior to berthing

Bunkering	Ship	Barge	Code	Remarks
1. The barge has obtained the necessary permissions to go alongside the receiving ship.				
2. The fenders have been checked, are in good order and there is no possibility of metal-to-metal contact.			R	
3. Adequate electrical insulating means are in place in the barge-to-barge ship connection. (34)				
4. All bunker hoses are in good condition and are appropriate for the service intended. (7)				

4. Checks prior to transfer

Bunkering	Ship	Barge	Code	Remarks
1. The barge is securely moored. (2)			R	
2. There is a safe means of access between the ship and barge. (1)			R	
3. Effective communications have been established between Responsible Officers. (3)			A R	(VHF/UHF Ch ___). Primary system Backup system Emergency stop signal
4. There is an effective watch on board the barge and on the ship receiving bunkers.				
5. Fire hoses and firefighting equipment on board the barge and ship are ready for immediate use. (5)				
6. All scuppers are effectively plugged. Temporarily removed scupper plugs will be monitored at all times. Drip trays are in position on decks around connections and bunker tank vents. (10) (11)			R	
7. Initial line up has been checked and unused bunker connections are blanked and fully bolted. (13)				
8. The transfer hose is properly rigged and fully bolted and secured to manifolds on ships and barges. (7)				
9. Overboard valves connected to the cargo system, engine room bilges and bunker lines are closed and sealed. (16)				
10. All cargo and bunker tank hatch lids are closed. (15)				
11. Bunker tank contents will be monitored at regular intervals.			A R	At intervals not exceeding ___ minutes
12. There is a supply of oil spill clean-up material readily available for immediate use.				

4. Checks prior to transfer *(continued)*

Bunkering	Ship	Barge	Code	Remarks
13. The main radio transmitter aerials are earthed and radars are switched off. (42)				
14. Fixed VHF/UHF transceivers and AIS equipment are on the correct power mode or switched off. (40)				
15. Smoking rooms have been identified and smoking restrictions are being observed. (36)			A R	Nominated smoking rooms: Tank _____ Barge _____
16. Naked light regulations are being observed. (37)				
17. All external doors and ports in the accommodation are closed. (17)				
18. Material Safety Data Sheets (MSDS) for the bunker transfer sheets have been exchanged where requested. (26)				

2 Example of oil transfer checklist for ice-covered waters

Vessel preparation

Valves:
Overboard discharge valves closed . . . . –
Valves not in use, secured . . . . –
Transfer valves operate through full range . . . . –
Transfer pipelines connections checked . . . . –
Double-check arrangements with crew . . . . –
Scuppers and freeing ports plugged . . . . –

Containment and absorbents:
Permanent containment . . . . –
Portable containment . . . . –
Absorbent material . . . . –

Accommodations:
Doors, deadlights/shutters/ports/vents closed . . . . –
Air conditioning recirculations mode . . . . –
Accommodation ventilation shut . . . . –

Navigation bridge including shore facility control area:
Hoist appropriate signals . . . . –
Announcement of impending transfer . . . . –

Restricted activities:
Hot work . . . . –
Smoking (except designated areas) . . . . –
Matches and lighters . . . . –
Portable electric lamps . . . . –
Equipment on extension cords . . . . –
–

Unless intrinsically safe, restricted use of:
Portable R/T sets . . . . –
Lamps . . . . –
Hand lamps . . . . –
Flashlights . . . . –
Other electrical devices . . . . –
Portable domestic radio . . . . –
Photographic flash equipment . . . . –

Vessel preparation *(continued)*	
Portable electronic calculator	–
Tape recorders	–
Wireless telephone	–
Other battery powered equipment	–
Radiating HF radios	–
Satcom and positioning systems	–
Engine room:	
Engine exhaust monitored for sparks	–
Spark arrestor functioning	–
Boiler soot blowing not permitted	–
Ground faults traced and isolated	–
Machinery spaces ventilation shut	–
Emergency procedures:	
Crew should be versed and rehearsed in:	
Emergency procedures	–
Firefighting equipment	–
Routine check of moorings and fenders	–
Safety equipment:	
Lifebuoys	–
Approved lifejackets/PFD	–
Appropriate cold weather clothing	–
Flashlights	–
First aid kit	–
Reflective material on personnel at night	–
Fire-fighting equipment:	
Fire extinguishers in place	–
Fire hose rolled out on deck	–
Fire-fighting systems, main and emergency pumps on standby	–
Lighting:	
Adequate lighting vessel and shore facilities	–
Work boat equipped with spotlight	–

Vessel preparation *(continued)*

Transfer hoses:

Valid hose certificate . . . . −

Indelibly marked: "For oil" . . . . −

Date of manufacture . . . . −

Bursting pressure . . . . −

Working pressure . . . . −

Date of last test . . . . −

Pressure applied under test . . . . −

Examine:

Condition of "O" ring/joints . . . . −

Hose to coupling clamps . . . . −

Complete hose system . . . . −

Hose strain relief system for floating hose . . . . −

Transfer checklist completed

3 Ship/Shore safety checklist

Ship's name _____

Berth _____ Port _____

Date of arrival _____ Port of arrival _____

Part 'A' – Bulk liquid general – physical checks

Bulk liquid general	Ship	Terminal	Code	Remarks
1. There is safe access between the ship and shore.			R	
2. The ship is securely moored.			R	
3. The agreed ship/shore communication system is operative.			A R	System: Backup system:
4. Emergency towing-off pennants are correctly rigged and positioned.			R	
5. The ship's fire hoses and firefighting equipment are positioned and ready for immediate use.			R	
6. The terminal's firefighting equipment is positioned and ready for immediate use.			R	
7. The ship's cargo and bunker hoses, pipelines and manifolds are in good condition, properly rigged and appropriate for the service intended.				
8. The terminal's cargo and bunker hoses or arms are in good condition, properly rigged and appropriate for the service intended.				
9. The cargo transfer system is sufficiently isolated and drained to allow safe removal of blank flanges prior to connection.				
10. Scuppers and save alls on board are effectively plugged and drip trays are in position and empty.				

Part 'A' – Bulk liquid general – physical checks *(continued)*

Bulk liquid general	Ship	Terminal	Code	Remarks
11. Temporarily removed scupper plugs will be constantly monitored.			R	
12. Shore spill containment and sumps are correctly managed.			R	
13. The ship's unused cargo and bunker connections are properly secured with blank flanges fully bolted.				
14. The terminal's unused cargo and bunker connections are properly secured with blank flanges fully bolted.				
15. All cargo, ballast and bunker tank lids are closed.				
16. Sea and overboard discharge valves when not in use, are closed and visibly secured.				
17. All external doors, ports and windows in the accommodation, stores and machinery spaces are closed. Engine room vents may be open.			R	
18. The ship's emergency fire control plans are located externally.				Location:

If the ship is fitted, or is required to be fitted, with an inert gas system (IGS), the following points should be physically checked:

Inert gas system	Ship	Terminal	Code	Remarks
19. Fixed IGS pressure and oxygen content recorders are working.			R	
20. All cargo tank atmospheres are at positive pressure with oxygen content of 8% or less by volume.			P R	

Part 'B' – Bulk liquid general – verbal verification

Bulk liquid general	Ship	Terminal	Code	Remarks
21. The ship is ready to move under its own power.			P R	
22. There is an effective deck watch in attendance on board and adequate supervision of operations on the ship and in the terminal.			R	
23. There are sufficient personnel on board and ashore to deal with an emergency.			R	
24. The procedures for cargo, bunker and ballast handling have been agreed.			A R	
25. The emergency signal and shutdown procedure to be used by the ship and shore have been explained and understood.			A	
26. Material Safety Data Sheets (MSDS) for the cargo transfer have been exchanged where requested.			P R	
27. The hazards associated with toxic substances in the cargo being handled have been identified and understood.				H_2s Content: Benzene Content:
28. An international shore fire connection has been provided.				
29. The agreed tank vetting system will be used.			A R	Method:
30. The requirements for closed operations have been agreed.			R	
31. The operation of the P/V system has been verified.				
32. Where a vapour return line is connected, operating parameters have been agreed.			A R	
33. Independent high level alarms, if fitted, are operational and have been tested.			A R	

Part 'B' – Bulk liquid general – verbal verification *(continued)*

Bulk liquid general	Ship	Terminal	Code	Remarks
34. Adequate electrical insulating means are in place in the ship/shore connection.			A R	
35. Shore lines are fitted with a non return valve, or procedures to avoid back filling have been discussed.			P R	
36. Smoking rooms have been identified and smoking requirements are being observed.			A R	
37. Naked light regulations are being observed.			A R	
38. Ship/shore telephones, mobile phones and pager requirements are being observed.			A R	
39. Hand torches (flashlights) are of an approved type.				
40. Fixed VHF/UHF transceivers and AIS equipment are on the correct power mode or switched off.				
41. Portable VHF/UHF transceivers are of an approved type.				
42. The ship's main radio transmitter aerials are earthed and radars are switched off.				
43. Electric cables to portable electrical equipment within the hazardous area are disconnected from power.				
44. Window type air conditioning units are disconnected.				
45. Positive pressure is being maintained inside the accommodation, and air conditioning intakes, which may permit the entry of cargo vapours, are closed.				
46. Measures have been taken to ensure sufficient mechanical ventilation in the pump room.			R	

Part 'B' – Bulk liquid general – verbal verification *(continued)*

Bulk liquid general	Ship	Terminal	Code	Remarks
47. There is provision for an emergency escape.				
48. The maximum wind and swell criteria for operations have been agreed.			A	Stop cargo at: Disconnect at: Unberth at:
49. Security protocols have been agreed between the Ship Security Officer and the Port Facility Security Officer, if appropriate.			A	
50. Where appropriate, procedures have been agreed for receiving nitrogen supplied from shore, either for inerting or purging ship's tanks, or for line clearing into the ship.			A P	

If the ship is fitted, or is required to be fitted, with an inert gas system (IGS) the following statements should be addressed:

Inert gas system	Ship	Terminal	Code	Remarks
51. The IGS is fully operational and in good working order.			P	
52. Deck seals, or equivalent, are in good working order.			R	
53. Liquid levels in pressure/vacuum breakers are correct.			R	
54. The fixed and portable oxygen analysers have been calibrated and are working properly.			R	
55. All the individual tank IG valves (if fitted) are correctly set and locked.			R	
56. All personnel in charge of cargo operations are aware that, in the case of failure of the inert gas plant, discharge operations should cease and the terminal be advised.			R	

Part 'B' – Bulk liquid general – verbal verification *(continued)*

If the ship is fitted with a crude oil washing (COW) system, and intends to crude oil wash, the following statements should be addressed:

Crude oil washing	Ship	Terminal	Code	Remarks
57. The pre arrival COW checklist, as contained in the approved COW manual, has been satisfactorily completed.				
58. The COW checklists for use before, during and after COW, as contained in the approved COW manual, are available and being used.			R	

If the ship is planning to tank clean alongside, the following statements should be addressed:

Tank cleaning	Ship	Terminal	Code	Remarks
59. Tank cleaning operations are planned during the ship's stay alongside the shore installation.	Yes/No*	Yes/No*		
60. If Yes, the procedures and approvals for tank cleaning have been agreed.				
61. Permission has been granted for gas freeing operations.	Yes/No*	Yes/No*		

* Delete Yes or No in each instance, as appropriate.

Part 'C' – Bulk liquid chemicals – verbal verification

Bulk liquid chemicals	Ship	Terminal	Code	Remarks
1. *Material Safety Data Sheets* are available giving the necessary data for the safe handling of the cargo.				
2. A manufacturer's inhibition certificate, where applicable, has been provided.			P	

Part 'C' – Bulk liquid chemicals – verbal verification *(continued)*

Bulk liquid chemicals	Ship	Terminal	Code	Remarks
3. Sufficient protective clothing and equipment (including self-contained breathing apparatus) is ready for immediate use and is suitable for the product being handled.				
4. Countermeasures against accidental personal contact with the cargo have been agreed.				
5. The cargo handling rate is compatible with the automatic shutdown system, if in use.			A	
6. Cargo system gauges and alarms are correctly set and in good order.				
7. Portable vapour detection instruments are readily available for the products being handled.				
8. Information on firefighting media and procedures has been exchanged.				
9. Transfer hoses are of suitable material, resistant to the action of the products being handled.				
10. Cargo handling is being performed with the permanent installed pipeline system.			P	
11. Where appropriate, procedures have been agreed for receiving nitrogen supplied from shore, either for inerting or purging ship's tanks, or for line clearing into the ship.			A P	
12. Material Safety Data Sheets are available giving the necessary data for the safe handling of the cargo.				
13. A manufacturer's inhibition certificate, where applicable, has been provided.			P	

Part 'C' – Bulk liquid chemicals – verbal verification *(continued)*

Bulk liquid chemicals	Ship	Terminal	Code	Remarks
14. The water spray system is ready for immediate use.				
15. There is sufficient protective equipment (including self-contained breathing apparatus) and protective clothing ready for immediate use.				
16. Hold and inter barrier spaces are properly inerted or filled with dry air, as required.				
17. All remote control valves are in working order.			A	
18. The required cargo pumps and compressors are in good order and the maximum working pressures have been agreed between ship and shore.			A	
19. Re-liquefacation or boil-off control equipment is in good order.				
20. The gas detection equipment has been properly set for the cargo, is calibrated, has been tested and is in good order.				
21. Cargo system gauges and alarms are correctly set and in good order.				
22. Emergency shutdown systems have been tested and are working properly.				
23. Ship and shore have informed each other of the closing rate of ESD valves, automatic valves or similar devices.				
24. Information has been exchanged between ship and shore on the maximum/minimum temperatures/pressures of the cargo to be handled.				

Part 'C' – Bulk liquid chemicals – verbal verification *(continued)*

Bulk liquid chemicals	Ship	Terminal	Code	Remarks
25. Cargo tanks are protected against inadvertent overfilling at all times while any cargo operations are in progress.				
26. The compressor room is properly ventilated, the electrical motor room is properly pressurized and the alarm system is working.				
27. Cargo tank relief valves are set correctly and actual relief valve settings are clearly and visibly displayed. (Record setting below.)				

Tank no. 1 [ ]   Tank no. 5 [ ]   Tank no. 8 [ ]

Tank no. 2 [ ]   Tank no. 6 [ ]   Tank no. 9 [ ]

Tank no. 3 [ ]   Tank no. 7 [ ]   Tank no. 10 [ ]

Tank no. 4 [ ]

4 Ship-to-ship transfer checklists

Checklist 1 – Pre-fixture information (for each ship)

SHIP-TO-SHIP TRANSFER CHECKLIST 1 – PRE-FIXTURE INFORMATION (FOR EACH SHIP) (BETWEEN EACH SHIP OPERATOR/CHARTERER AND ORGANIZER)			
Ship's name _____ IMO no. _____			
Ship operator:	Ship charterer:	STS organizer:	
Preferred contact no. (e.g. INMARSAT)		Ship operator's confirmation	Remarks
1. What is the LOA? What is parallel body length at loaded and ballast draughts?			
2. Will the transfer be conducted underway and, if so, can the ship maintain about five knots for a minimum of two hours?			
3. Is the ship's manifold arrangement in accordance with OCIMF *Recommendations for oil tanker manifolds and associated equipment*?			
4. Is the ship's lifting equipment in accordance with OCIMF *Recommendations for oil tanker manifolds and associated equipment*?			
5. What is the maximum and minimum expected height of the cargo manifold from the waterline during the transfer?			
6. Will sufficient manpower be provided for all stages of the operation?			
7. Are enclosed fairleads and mooring bitts in accordance with OCIMF *Mooring equipment guidelines* and are they of sufficient number?			
8. Can the ship supplying the moorings provide all lines on winch drums?			
9. If moorings are wires or high modulus fibre ropes, are they fitted with synthetic tails at least eleven metres in length?			

Checklist 1 – Pre-fixture information (for each ship) *(continued)*

10. Full-sized mooring bitts of sufficient strength are suitably located near all enclosed fairleads to receive mooring ropes' eyes?		
11. Both sides of the ship are clear of any overhanging projections including bridge wings?		
12. The transfer area has been agreed?		
FOR DISCHARGING SHIP/RECEIVING SHIP (Delete as appropriate)		
Name:		
Rank:		
Signature: Date:		

This form should not be substituted for other required checklists. If this form is used, it should be used in its entirety.

Checklist 2 – Before operations commence

SHIP-TO-SHIP TRANSFER CHECKLIST 2 – BEFORE OPERATIONS COMMENCE			
Discharging ship's name:			
Receiving ship's name:			
Date of transfer:			
	Discharging ship checked	Receiving ship checked	Remarks
1. The two ships have been advised by shipowners that Checklist 1 has been completed satisfactorily?			
2. Personnel comply with rest requirements of ILO 180, STCW or national regulations as appropriate?			
3. Radio communications are established?			
4. Language of operations has been agreed?			
5. The rendezvous position off the transfer area is agreed?			
6. Berthing and mooring procedures are agreed, including fender positions and number/type of ropes to be provided by each ship?			
7. The system and method of electrical insulation between ships has been agreed?			
8. The ships are upright and at a suitable trim without any overhanging projections?			
9. Engines, steering gear and navigational equipment have been tested and found in good order?			

Checklist 2 – Before operations commence *(continued)*

10. Ship's boilers and tubes have been cleared of soot and it is understood that during STS operations tubes must not be blown?			
11. Engineers have been briefed on engine speed (and speed adjustment) requirements?			
12. Weather forecasts have been obtained for the transfer area?			
13. Hose lifting equipment is suitable and ready for use?			
14. Cargo transfer hoses are properly tested and certified and in apparent good condition?			
15. Fenders and associated equipment are visually in apparent good order?			
16. The crew has been briefed on the mooring procedure?			
17. The contingency plan is agreed?			
18. Local authorities have been advised about the operation?			
19. A navigational warning has been broadcast?			
20. The other ship has been advised that Checklist 2 is satisfactorily completed?			

FOR DISCHARGING SHIP/RECEIVING SHIP (Delete as appropriate)

Name:

Rank:

Signature: Date:

Note that items 13, 14 and 15 can only be checked by the vessel that has them on board. This form should not be substituted for other required checklists. If this form is used, it should be used in its entirety.

Checklist 3 – Before run-in and mooring

SHIP-TO-SHIP TRANSFER CHECKLIST 3 – BEFORE RUN-IN AND MOORING			
Discharging ship's name:			
Receiving ship's name:			
Date of transfer:			
	Discharging ship checked	Receiving ship checked	Remarks
1. Checklist 2 has been satisfactorily completed?			
2. Primary fenders are floating in their proper place? Fender pennants are in order?			
3. Secondary fenders are in place, if required?			
4. Overside protrusions on side of berthing are retracted?			
5. A proficient helmsman is at the wheel?			
6. Cargo manifold connections are ready and marked?			
7. Course and speed information has been exchanged and is understood?			
8. Ship's speed adjustment is controlled by changes to revolutions and/or propeller pitch?			[Specify]
9. Navigational signals are displayed?			
10. Adequate lighting is available?			
11. Power is on winches and windlass and they are in good order?			
12. Rope messengers, rope stoppers and heaving lines are ready for use?			
13. All mooring lines are ready?			

Checklist 3 – Before run-in and mooring *(continued)*

14. All mooring personnel are in position?			
15. Communications are established with mooring personnel?			
16. The anchor on opposite side to transfer is ready for dropping?			
17. The other ship has been advised that Checklist 3 is satisfactorily completed?			
FOR DISCHARGING SHIP/RECEIVING SHIP (Delete as appropriate)			
Name:			
Rank:			
Signature: Date:			

This form should not be substituted for other required checklists. If this form is used, it should be used in its entirety.

Checklist 4 – Before cargo transfer

SHIP-TO-SHIP TRANSFER CHECKLIST 4 – BEFORE CARGO TRANSFER			
Discharging ship's name:			
Receiving ship's name:			
Date of transfer:			
	Discharging ship checked	Receiving ship checked	Remarks
1. The *ISGOTT Ship/Shore Safety Checklist* has been satisfactorily completed?			
2. Procedures for transfer of personnel have been agreed?			
3. The gangway (if used) is in a good position and well secured?			
4. An inter-ship communication system is agreed?			
5. Emergency signals and shutdown procedures are agreed?			
6. An engine room watch will be maintained throughout transfer and the main engine ready for immediate use?			
7. Fire axes or suitable cutting equipment is in position at fore and aft mooring stations?			
8. A bridge watch and/or an anchor watch are established?			
9. Officers in charge of the cargo transfer on both ships are identified and posted?			
10. A deck watch is established to pay particular attention to moorings, fenders, hoses, manifold observation and cargo pump controls?			

Checklist 4 – Before cargo transfer *(continued)*

11. The initial cargo transfer rate is agreed with the other ship?			
12. The maximum cargo transfer rates agreed with the other ship?			
13. The topping-off rate is agreed with the other ship?			
14. Cargo hoses are well supported?			
15. Tools required for rapid disconnection are located at the cargo manifold?			
16. Details of the previous cargo of the receiving ship have been given to the discharging ship?			
17. The other ship has been advised that Checklist 4 is satisfactorily completed?			
FOR DISCHARGING SHIP/RECEIVING SHIP (Delete as appropriate)			
Name:			
Rank:			
Signature: Date:			

This form should not be substituted for other required checklists. If this form is used, it should be used in its entirety.

Checklist 5 – Before unmooring

SHIP-TO-SHIP TRANSFER CHECKLIST 5 – BEFORE UNMOORING			
Discharging ship's name:			
Receiving ship's name:			
Date of transfer:			
	Discharging ship checked	Receiving ship checked	Remarks
1. Cargo hoses are properly drained prior to hose disconnection?			
2. Cargo hoses or manifolds are blanked?			
3. The transfer side of the ship is clear of obstructions (including hose lifting equipment)?			
4. Secondary fenders are correctly positioned and secured for departure?			
5. The method of unberthing and of letting go moorings has been agreed with the other ship?			
6. Fenders, including fender pennants, are in good order?			
7. Power is on winches and windlass?			
8. There are rope messengers and rope stoppers at all mooring stations?			
9. The crew are standing by at their mooring stations?			
10. Communications are established with mooring personnel and with the other ship?			
11. Shipping traffic in the area has been checked?			

Checklist 5 – Before unmooring *(continued)*

12. Main engine(s) and steering gear have been tested and are in a state of readiness for departure?			
13. Mooring personnel have been instructed to let go only as requested by the manoeuvring ship?			
14. Navigational warnings have been cancelled (when clear of the other ship)?			
15. The other ship has been advised that Checklist 5 is satisfactorily completed?			
FOR DISCHARGING SHIP/RECEIVING SHIP (Delete as appropriate)			
Name:			
Rank:			
Signature: Date:			

This form should not be substituted for other required checklists. If this form is used, it should be used in its entirety.